CRAFTY HISTORY
Activity Book

Sue and Steve Weatherill

CONTENTS

(Not in chronological order through time!)

3

WHAT DO THESE WORDS MEAN?

Acrylic paints – use acrylic paints as they coat plastic better than ordinary paint. For projects that need a metal finish, use acrylic chrome spray paint. Ask an adult to help you with this.

Bubble plastic – this is great for craft projects. If you can't find any from old packaging, you can buy it cheaply. Bubble envelopes are very useful, too, for some projects but ask first if you can use them.

Paper paste – to make a paste: put 1 cup of cheap flour in a bowl. Add 1 teaspoon of salt and slowly mix in 2 cups of lukewarm water. Or you can buy cellulose paste powder and follow the instructions.

PVA glue – this is used not just as glue but also as a primer to stop paint sinking into a surface. It also makes surfaces waterproof. To make primer, mix some glue with three times the amount of water. Keep any left over in a labelled jar. Wash brushes as soon as possible after use.

Sandpaper – sanding a surface helps paint or glue to stick to it. Rub the surface with rough sandpaper or a sanding block.

Scoring – doing this makes card easier to fold. Hold a ruler along the line and run the blunt side of some scissors lightly along it. If the card needs to bend more, do this again. You can use a compass point instead of scissors.

 **TAKE CARE!**

Be extra careful and have an adult standing by where you see a red star. When using a craft knife, put a board under whatever you are cutting and use a ruler to help guide the knife.

 Look out for this symbol on certain pages. This means that the recipe contains nuts.

WHAT YoU WILL NEED

You will be able to find many of the materials mentioned in this book in amongst your recycling. If you have space, save them in a box at home. Here are some tips on how to make sure you don't waste those valuable, crafting materials:

You can flatten cardboard boxes and cereal packets to save space. Rinse plastic bottles and leave them to dry. Prepare an area to work in and have lots of old newspapers handy if you are using glue and paints.

Whatever you choose to make first you'll need plenty of packaging so it's a good idea to start collecting it in advance. Ask people to save things for you instead of throwing them away.

EGYPTIAN ACTIVITIES
HOW TO MAKE MAGIC AMULETS

Amulets were sacred lucky charms for the living and the dead. The ankh was the hieroglyphic symbol of life. It meant health and happiness. The eye of Horus, or wedjat eye, was a powerful protection against evil. The scarab beetle was the most popular amulet. It was the symbol of birth and eternal life.

YOU'LL NEED:
Scissors, tracing paper, masking tape, pencil, paper, PVA glue, card, paints, felt-tips or metallic pens, decorative string or magnetic strip.

Are you looking at me?

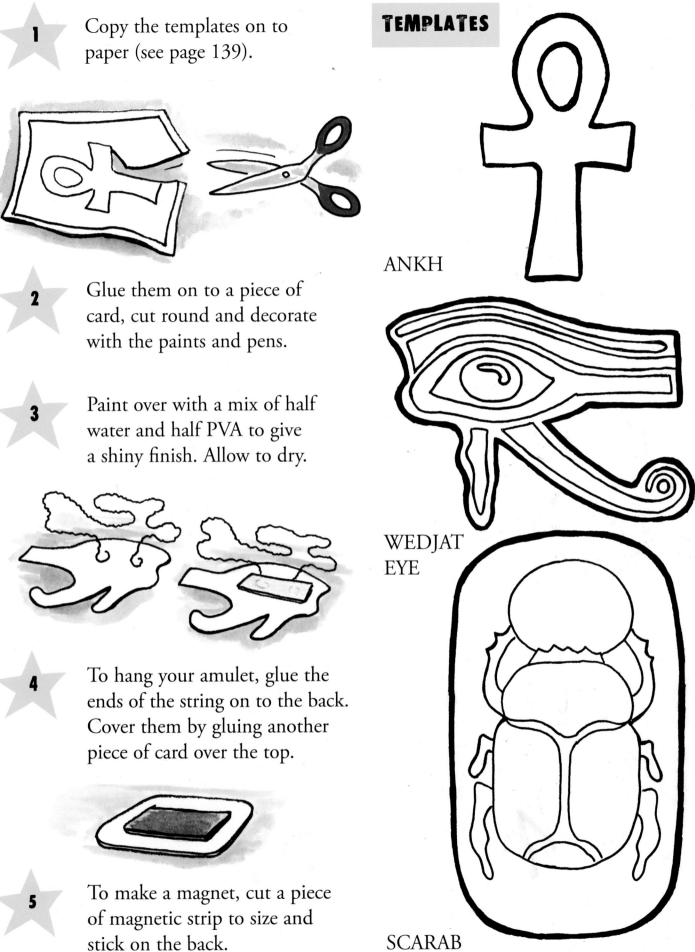

1 Copy the templates on to paper (see page 139).

2 Glue them on to a piece of card, cut round and decorate with the paints and pens.

3 Paint over with a mix of half water and half PVA to give a shiny finish. Allow to dry.

4 To hang your amulet, glue the ends of the string on to the back. Cover them by gluing another piece of card over the top.

5 To make a magnet, cut a piece of magnetic strip to size and stick on the back.

ANKH

WEDJAT EYE

SCARAB

WHO PUT THE 'Y' IN PYRAMIDS?

Egypt is known for its pyramids. The most famous are the pyramids of Giza and the biggest of them is the Great Pyramid. It is the first, and last remaining, of the seven wonders of the ancient world.

We think it was built as the tomb to beat all tombs for the Pharaoh Khufu (or Cheops).

SPHINX

I was there, but I'm not telling.

It is 146 metres high and was the biggest building in the world for nearly 4,500 years.

It's still the heaviest at 6½ million tons!

The outer stones fit so perfectly that a knife can't be pushed between them.

It contains about 2.3 million blocks of stone. Each weighs about 2 tons.

Inside are secret passages leading to a central burial chamber.

PYRAMAGIC

In the Middle Ages, it was thought that the stones had been flown into position after being put on sheets of papyrus like magic carpets.

Left a bit.

PYRAMAD?
Today, people with unusual ideas about the pyramids are called pyramidiots.

They think that spacemen built them…

…or the man from Atlantis, (a lost land drowned by the great flood)…

…and that the Ancient Egyptians sailed over to America in a papyrus boat and showed the Mexicans how to build their pyramids.

Muchos graciás.

PYRAMEX

8

The very first pyramid was built about 2,650 BC to be the tomb of Pharaoh Zoser.

It was seen as his stairway to heaven when he died.

How did the Ancient Egyptians make something so big, yet have such accurate measurements?

They only had copper, stone and wooden tools.

Ow!

We think they floated giant stones down the Nile on barges, then along canals to the pyramid.

Then the stone blocks were levered on to wooden sledges, wooden rollers or round stones.

Finally they were pulled up ramps built around the pyramid.

Watch the corner, buddy!

Ramps made of small stones or mud bricks.

But nobody has fully explained how the Great Pyramid was built. See what you can find out.

Using the wonders of today like robots, satellites and DNA, we are learning more and more about the wonders of the past. Soon, someone will solve the mysteries of the Great Pyramid. It could be you!

PYRAMEDICS

HOW TO MAKE A PYRAMID

Have a go at making your own Great Pyramid. Make a small one first to see how it works, then make a bigger one. It could even be big enough to get inside and frighten people using a ghostly voice! Give your Great Pyramid an aged look by tearing off the paper in places to show the corrugations underneath. Use your paints to make it look old or new.

YOU'LL NEED:

Scissors, craft knife, glue, ruler, pencil, tracing paper, masking tape, ballpoint pen, thin card, large piece of corrugated cardboard and drawing-pin.

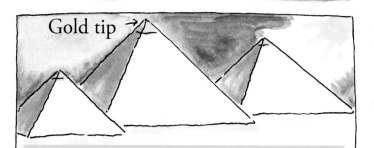

Gold tip →

WHEN THEY WERE NEW, THE PYRAMIDS WERE COVERED IN BRILLIANT WHITE LIMESTONE WHICH WOULD HAVE GLINTED IN THE SUNLIGHT. WHAT A MAGNIFICENT SIGHT!

1 Copy the template on to the card (following the instructions on page 139).

Tab to glue

TEMPLATE

2 Cut it out and pin to the centre of the large sheet of cardboard.

3 Use your ruler to extend the five blue lines by equal lengths. Draw four lines to join the ends.

4 Remove the template and draw the lines to the centre.

5 Extend the tab, cut out, score, fold and glue.

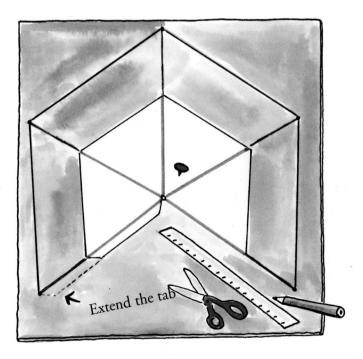

Extend the tab

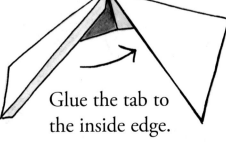

Glue the tab to the inside edge.

11

HOW TO MAKE A POP-UP MUMMY

The Ancient Egyptians believed in life after death, but only if their bodies were perfectly preserved. These were embalmed and wrapped in linen bandages. The preserved body was called a mummy.

YOU'LL NEED:
2 sheets A4 card, pencil, tracing paper, masking tape, ballpoint pen, scissors, ruler, double-sided tape, paints and felt-tips.

EVERYONE LOVES MUMMIES. THEY ARE FUNNY AND SCARY. THE FIRST MUMMY FILM WAS MADE OVER 100 YEARS AGO!

Tut toot!

Happy mummy's day!

Back of pop-up

Tab 1

Double-sided tape

Fold out

Fold in

Tab 2

Double-sided tape

1 Copy the template on to one sheet of card (see the instructions on page 139).

2 Cut round the bold outline. Score and fold along the blue lines. Fold the other piece of A4 card in half.

3 Draw a rectangle 10 x 2 cm, 3 cm from the edges of the card.

4 Using double-sided tape stick tab 1 carefully to the rectangle.

5 Fold the pop-up flat and put double-sided tape on the back of tab 2.

6 Press the card shut. Open to activate the mummy. Decorate your card using the templates on page 140 and paints and felt-tips.

DRAW LIKE AN EGYPTIAN

There is nothing quite like Egyptian art. The artists had to follow strict rules. They drew using a square grid and each part of the body would take up its correct number of squares. If someone in the picture was important they were drawn larger than the others!

YOU'LL NEED:
Squared paper, ruler, pencil, paints, gold and silver pens.

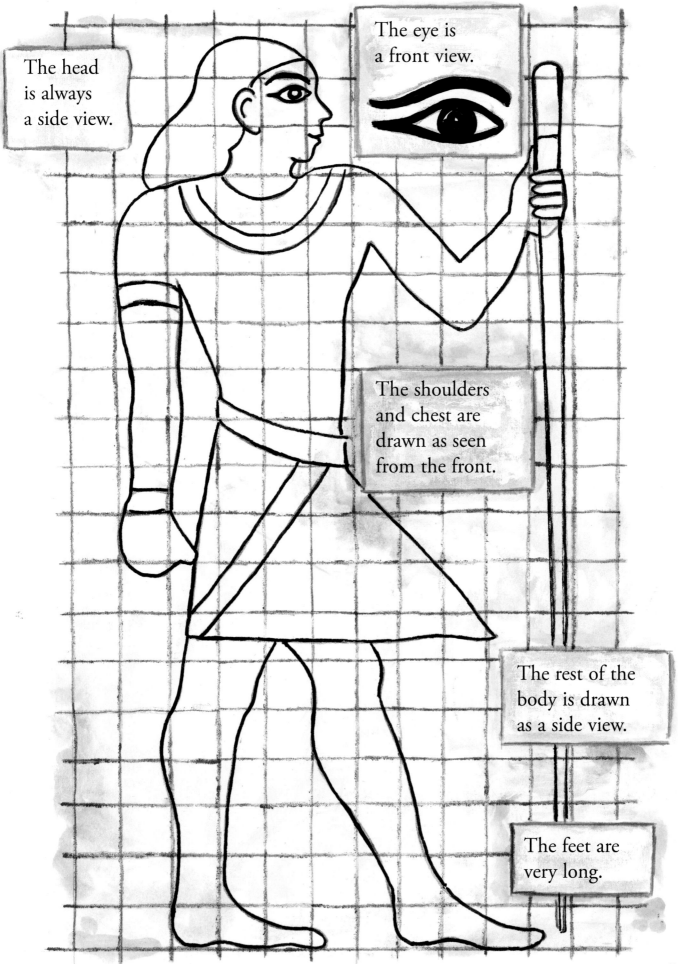

The head is always a side view.

The eye is a front view.

The shoulders and chest are drawn as seen from the front.

The rest of the body is drawn as a side view.

The feet are very long.

ANCIENT EGYPT

Egypt is the world's largest oasis. A thin strip of fertile land, it stretches for 1,200 kilometres along the banks of Africa's longest river, the Nile. The Ancient Egyptians called their country 'the gift of the Nile'. The fertile black land by the river they called Kemi. The harsh, endless desert which hemmed them in, they called Desret, the red land.

BC

3,100 BC

Earliest recorded history of Egypt. Hieroglyphs first used.

Walking fish glyph (No translation yet!)

2,700–2,400 BC

The Great Pyramids built at Giza (near Cairo).

AD

AD 1799

The Rosetta Stone is found which leads to Champollion cracking the code to reading the hieroglyphs in AD 1822.

Champion, Champollion!

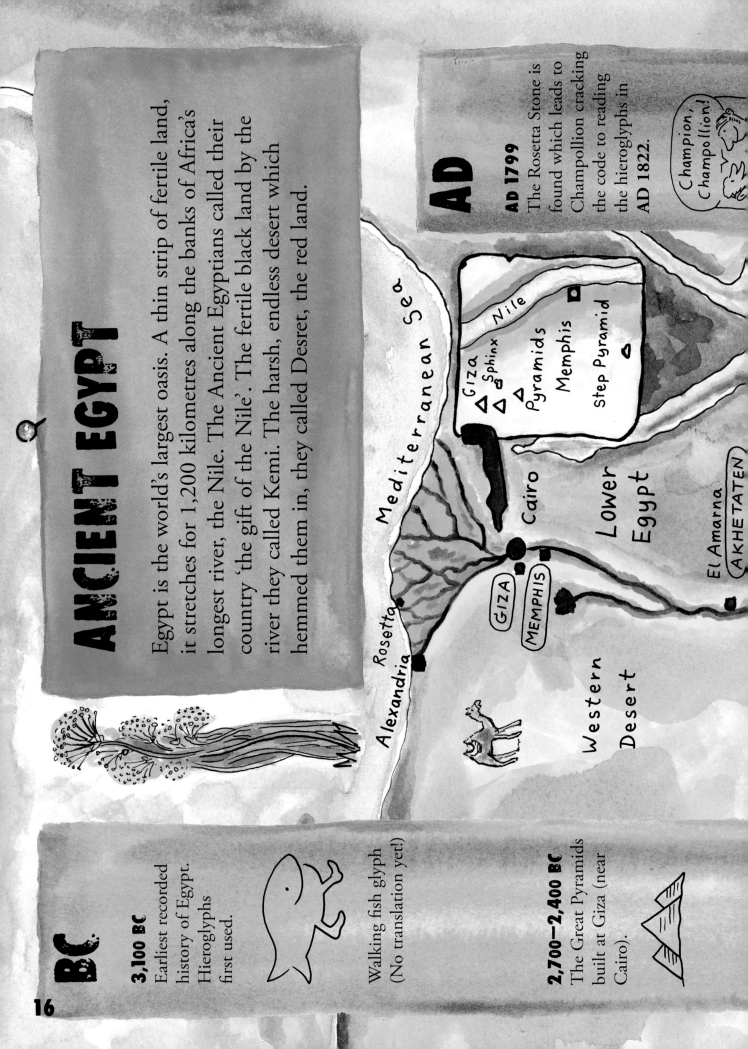

Mediterranean Sea

Rosetta

Alexandria

GIZA

MEMPHIS

Cairo

Nile

Giza
Sphinx
Pyramids
Memphis
Step Pyramid

Lower Egypt

El Amarna (AKHETATEN)

Western Desert

AD 1922
The tomb of Tut-ankh-amun is discovered in the Valley of the Kings.

Well, well, well.

Red Sea

Rain is almost unknown in this strange land. The fields are watered by ditches bringing water from the Nile. Before the building of the great dams at Aswan, the Nile flooded every year. This left the fields covered with rich, dark, fertilizing mud which came all the way from the heart of Africa.

Eastern Desert

DENDERA

KARNAK
Luxor

THEBES

KOM OMBO

Aswan

ELEPHANTINE ISLAND

High Dam

Nubia

Sudan

ABYDOS

Nile

Kings' Valley

Deir el Bahri

Queen's Valley

Ramesseum

Colossi of Memnon

Mr Ahmed's Bicycle Hire Shop

Karnak Temple

Luxor Temple

Ferry

16 km

ABU SIMBEL

1,324 BC
The boy-king Tut-ankh-amun buried in Kings' Valley or Valley of the Kings (near Luxor).

30 BC
Cleopatra, last queen of Egypt dies. Egypt becomes part of the Roman Empire.

Ouch!

HOW TO MAKE ANCIENT EGYPTIAN SWEETS

The Egyptians did not have sweets as we know them. Although sugar cane is grown along the Nile today, there was no sugar in Ancient Egypt so people used honey, dates or fruit juice to sweeten food. This ancient recipe was found written on a piece of broken pottery.

KITCHENWARE YOU'LL NEED:

Food processor, large bowl, large plate, 2 teaspoons, tablespoon and small paper cases.

INGREDIENTS YOU'LL NEED:

200 g stoned dates, 125 g walnut pieces, 4 tablespoons clear honey, 1 teaspoon ground cinnamon, ground cumin (optional), and ground almonds for coating.

THE ANCIENT EGYPTIANS USED GROUND CUMIN. IT MAY NOT BE TO YOUR TASTE SO WHY NOT PUT HALF THE MIXTURE IN ANOTHER BOWL AND ADD 1/8 – 1/4 TEASPOON TO ONE AND MIX IN WELL.

Am I old enough to help?

1 First, wash your hands.

2 Ask an adult to help with using the food processor. With the machine set to high, chop the dates till they go into a ball (about 15 seconds). Take them out and put in the bowl.

3 Put the walnuts in the machine and chop for about 10 seconds. Put the dates back into the processor with the walnuts.

4 With the machine set to medium, add the honey and cinnamon through the funnel.

5 Put the mixture back into the large bowl.

6 Pour some ground almonds on to the plate. Roll a teaspoonful of mixture in them until well coated. Use two teaspoons to do this.

7 Put the sweets into small paper cases. Store in the fridge.

19

HOW TO MAKE A JEWELLED COLLAR

These beautiful collars were worn by both men and women. Kings and queens and very rich people wore collars made with gold and precious stones. Poorer people made them out of flowers. When the flowers died, they made another one!

YOU'LL NEED:
40 x 40 cm white poly cotton, PVA glue mixed with water 1:4, paintbrush, old cardboard, masking tape, pencil, felt-tips, pegs, scissors and string or cord.

1 Lay the material over the old cardboard and paint with PVA mix. Leave two corners so you can pick it up. Hang up to dry. This may take several hours.

⭐ **2** Line up one corner of the fabric over the template (below). Secure fabic with masking tape. Trace template on to the fabric with a pencil.

⭐ **3** Rotate fabric so next corner lines up with template. Tape in place and trace. Repeat twice more.

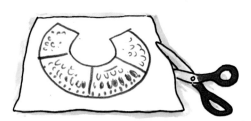

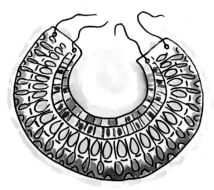

⭐ **4** Colour with markers, and go around each shape in black to give a bold effect. Cut out the collar.

⭐ **5** To wear your collar: make four holes, as shown, and thread with cord for a fastening.

TEMPLATE

Line up corner of material with corner of the page.

HOW TO MAKE DECORATIVE ARMBANDS

As well as collars, the Ancient Egyptians liked to wear armbands and bracelets, decorated in patterns of bright colours.

YOU'LL NEED:
Plastic drink bottle about 5-7 cm wide, scissors, craft knife, rough sandpaper, acrylic paints including white and metallic pens.

1 Wash the bottle and remove the label.

2 Get an adult to help you cut a strip from the bottle.

3 Cut through and round off the corners.

4 Rub sandpaper all over the plastic. Paint with white acrylic paint.

5 When dry, use acrylic paints and pens to decorate with an Egyptian pattern.

HAVE FUN WITH HIEROGLYPHS

The Ancient Egyptians invented one of the very first written languages – a picture language of beautifully drawn birds and animals – called hieroglyphs. The template sheet on page 140 contains 27 glyphs known as the Hieroglyphic Alphabet. Each one stood for a sound. Pages 24-25 show how they look painted on the walls of tombs and temples. Underneath there is a guide with approximate sounds in English. You can have fun writing English in hieroglyphs just like a secret code.

VWLS
THE ANCIENT EGYPTIANS DIDN'T USE VOWELS (A, E, I, O, U) AS WE DO – A BIT LIKE TXTNG!

THEY ALSO WROTE ON PAPER MADE FROM A REED CALLED PAPYRUS.

TOP TIP – TOP TIP
There are over 700 different glyphs. See if you can find out the meanings of some more.

Don't worry, nobody knows exactly how Ancient Egyptian sounded.

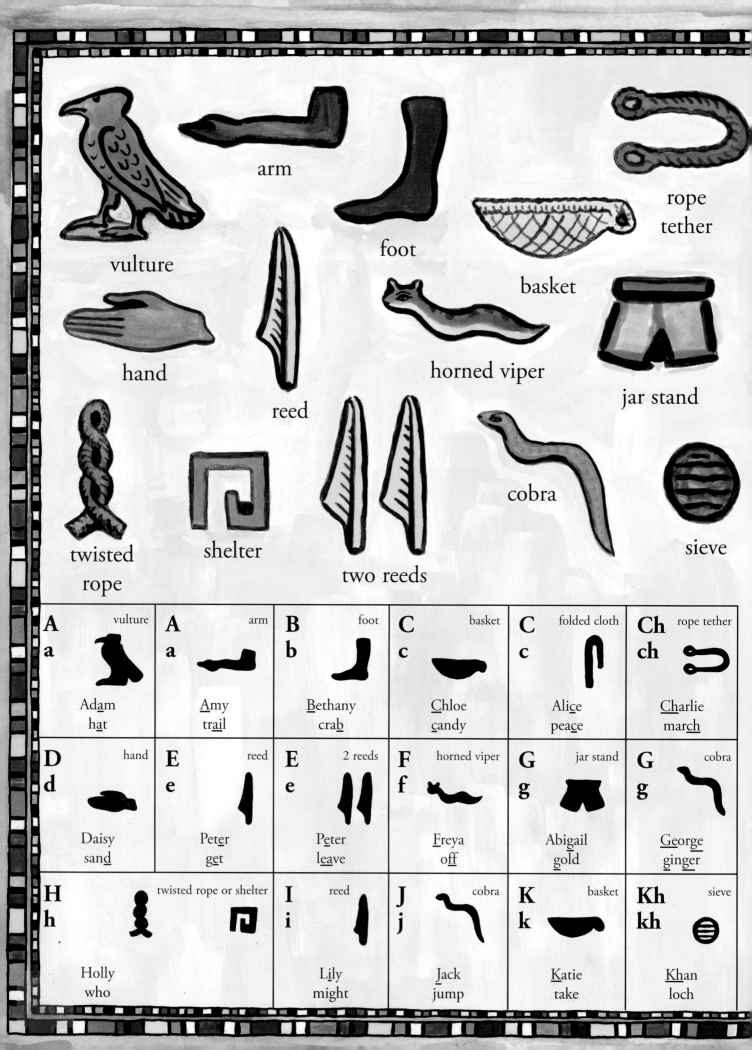

vulture

arm

foot

rope tether

basket

horned viper

jar stand

hand

reed

cobra

twisted rope

shelter

two reeds

sieve

A a — vulture	A a — arm	B b — foot	C c — basket	C c — folded cloth	Ch ch — rope tether
Ad**a**m h**a**t	**A**my tr**ai**l	**B**ethany cra**b**	**Ch**loe **c**andy	Ali**c**e pea**c**e	**Ch**arlie mar**ch**

D d — hand	E e — reed	E e — 2 reeds	F f — horned viper	G g — jar stand	G g — cobra
Daisy san**d**	P**e**t**e**r **ge**t	P**e**t**e**r l**ea**ve	**F**reya o**ff**	Abi**g**ail **g**old	**G**eorge **g**inger

H h — twisted rope or shelter	I i — reed	J j — cobra	K k — basket	Kh kh — sieve
Holly w**h**o	**Li**ly m**i**ght	**J**ack **j**ump	**K**atie ta**k**e	**Kh**an lo**ch**

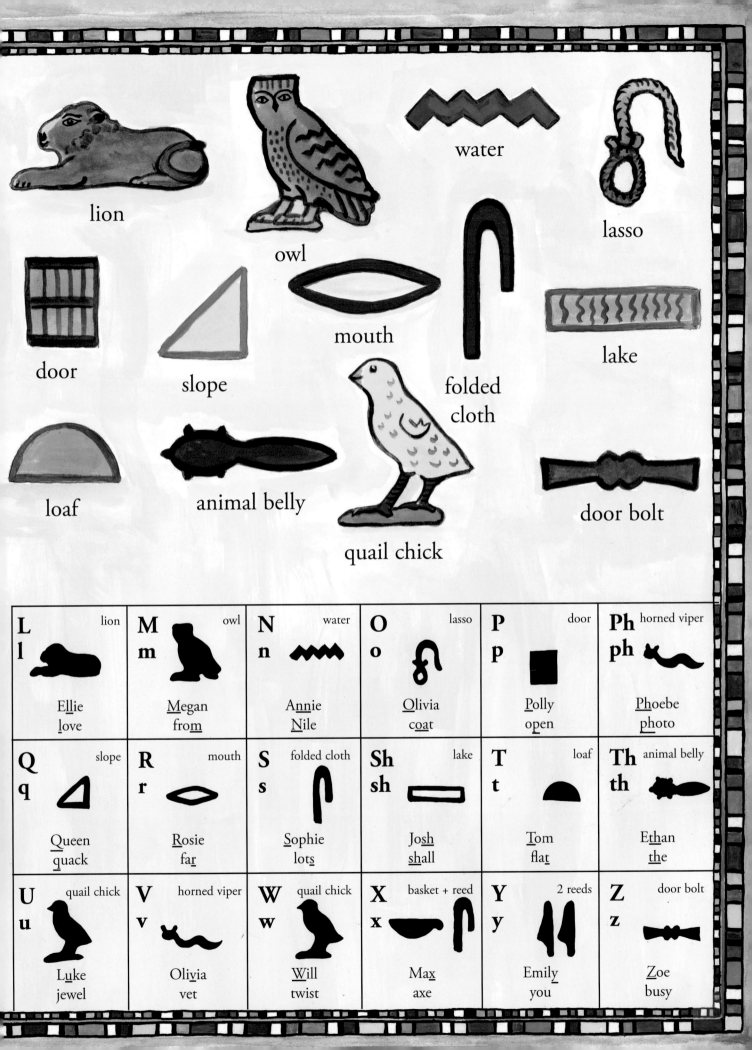

lion

owl

water

lasso

door

mouth

folded cloth

lake

slope

loaf

animal belly

quail chick

door bolt

L l lion Ellie <u>l</u>ove	**M** m owl <u>M</u>egan fro<u>m</u>	**N** n water A<u>nn</u>ie <u>N</u>ile	**O** o lasso <u>O</u>livia c<u>o</u>at	**P** p door <u>P</u>olly o<u>p</u>en	**Ph** ph horned viper <u>Ph</u>oebe <u>ph</u>oto
Q q slope <u>Q</u>ueen <u>q</u>uack	**R** r mouth <u>R</u>osie fa<u>r</u>	**S** s folded cloth <u>S</u>ophie lot<u>s</u>	**Sh** sh lake Jo<u>sh</u> <u>sh</u>all	**T** t loaf <u>T</u>om fla<u>t</u>	**Th** th animal belly E<u>th</u>an <u>th</u>e
U u quail chick L<u>u</u>ke jewel	**V** v horned viper Oli<u>v</u>ia <u>v</u>et	**W** w quail chick <u>W</u>ill t<u>w</u>ist	**X** x basket + reed Ma<u>x</u> a<u>x</u>e	**Y** y 2 reeds Emil<u>y</u> <u>y</u>ou	**Z** z door bolt <u>Z</u>oe bu<u>z</u>y

HOW TO MAKE A CARTOUCHE

The names of pharaohs were written inside a rope loop called a cartouche. Let everyone know whose room it is by making a cartouche for your bedroom door. You may have to translate it underneath – not everyone can read Ancient Egyptian!

YOU'LL NEED:
Paper, pencil, ruler, jar, scissors, card, paint and felt-tips, glue, sticky tack or double-sided tape.

DISCOVERING THE NAME OF CLEOPAT(D)RA IN A CARTOUCHE HELPED TO SOLVE THE MYSTERY OF THE HIEROGLYPHS. THEIR MEANING HAD BEEN LOST FOR 1,500 YEARS.

IT HAD BEEN LIKE SOMEONE RECORDING THEIR LIFE ON VIDEOTAPE, THEN BUYING A DVD PLAYER AND FORGETTING HOW TO USE THE OLD MACHINE.

My name is Khufu, the pharaoh who built the Great Pyramid.

1 Choose the hieroglyphs from pages 24-25 which match the sounds in your name.

2 Draw them lightly in pencil on the paper.

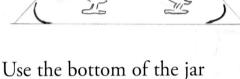

3 Use the ruler to draw a frame round the hieroglyphs.

4 Use the bottom of the jar to draw the corners.

5 Paint or use felt-tips to colour the hieroglyphs. Use pages 24-25 as a guide.

6 Paint or use felt-tips to make the frame look like rope.

7 Glue the cartouche on to card and cut it out.

8 Stick to your door using tack or double-sided tape.

GREEK ACTIVITIES
HOW TO MAKE A MAGIC BRACELET

Amphitrite was the wife of the sea god, Poseidon, and queen of the seas. Dolphins helped Poseidon to win her heart by speaking softly to her of his love. There were many dolphins living in the Mediterranean then. In the Greek myths, they guided ships and took messages for Poseidon.

He loves you.

Yeah, yeah, yeah!

YOU'LL NEED:
A clean plastic pot, sandpaper, scissors, acrylic paint and brushes, gold and silver pens, PVA glue, plaster filler and stencil.

1 Choose a plastic pot wide enough to get your hand through.

2 Carefully cut off the bottom. Watch out for sharp edges!

3 Roughen the outer surface with the sandpaper and paint with white acrylic paint.

4 Decorate using the dolphin template on page 141, gold and silver pens and paint.

5 You could mix a very small amount of plaster filler and PVA with the paint to make the dolphins stand out.

TOP TIP

When you have finished decorating and it is dry, paint over with undiluted craft glue. This will protect it and keep the colours bright.

KAΘ

6 Leave a space to write your name using the Greek letters on pages 36-37.

29

HOW TO MAKE A MEDUSA HEAD SHIELD

Meet Medusa the Gorgon. Just one look will turn you to stone but, by looking at her only in the reflection on his highly polished shield, Perseus was able to cut off her head. Perseus gave the head to the goddess Athene. She put it on the front of her shield.

1 Glue the pieces of cardboard together with the corrugations going in opposite ways.

2 Draw a circle 44 cm in diameter on the cardboard. Use a pencil tied to the nail. Then cut it out.

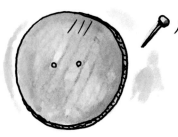

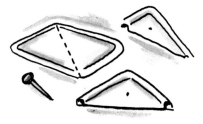

3 Make 2 small holes about 10 cm apart near the centre of the shield.

4 Cut 2 eye shapes from the tub lid. Make a small hole in each.

Front   Back

5 Glue these over the holes in the shield.

6 Thread the string through the eye holes. Leave a loop at the back to form a handle.

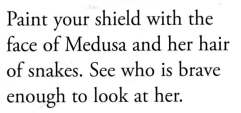

I have two older sisters!

7 Tie a bead or button to each end.

8 Paint your shield with the face of Medusa and her hair of snakes. See who is brave enough to look at her.

HOW TO EAT AND DRINK LIKE THE GODS

After a hard day's battling, the great gods on Mount Olympus needed a little refreshment. They didn't eat ordinary food as mortal people did. They had ambrosia and nectar. It was thought that if a mortal ate it, they would become a god!

KITCHENWARE YOU'LL NEED

Ambrosia: jug, 2 tablespoons, large bowl, whisk, large metal spoon and 4-6 serving dishes.
Nectar: blender, 2 tablespoons and 2 glasses.

INGREDIENTS YOU'LL NEED

Ambrosia: 1 lemon jelly (non-vegetarian), 2 tablespoons clear honey and 600 ml double cream.
Nectar: 300 ml milk, 1 tablespoon clear honey and 4 tablespoons vanilla ice-cream.

AMBROSIA

 1 First, wash your hands.

★ Make the jelly according to the instructions on the packet.

3 Add the honey, stirring well.

4 In the large bowl, whisk the cream until it stands in soft peaks.

5 Slowly fold the jelly into the cream.

6 Pour into the dishes and leave to set.

NECTAR

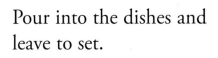

 ★ Put all the ingredients into the blender and blend for 10 seconds.

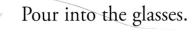 **2** Pour into the glasses.

HOW TO DECORATE YOUR DRINK

The Ancient Greeks would think it strange to throw away containers as we do today. They decorated their drinking cups and vases with exciting stories from the myths. Many of them have beautiful shapes. Use your stencils to transform some modern containers into Ancient Greek works of art.

YOU'LL NEED:
Clean plastic containers with tops, drinks cans, sandpaper, stencils, pencil, acrylic paints and brushes, flour and varnish (optional).

TOP TIP - TOP TIP
Keep the container tops. They are handy to hold on to when painting.

1 Roughen the surface of your containers or drinks cans with the sandpaper. This will help the paint to stick.

2 Hold your container by its top or with a pencil in the top of a can. Paint with white acrylic paint.

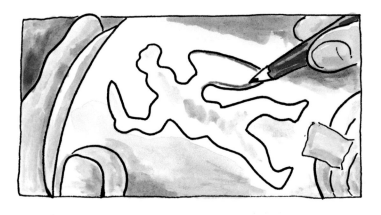

3 Hold your stencil in place and draw the outline in pencil. (A friend could help to hold it steady for you.)

4 Paint in the shapes and build them out by adding a bit of flour to the paint to thicken it.

5 Leave to dry well before adding more thick paint.

6 You can varnish it to keep the colours bright. Make sure the paint is completely dry first.

HOW TO WRITE ANCIENT GREEK

The Ancient Greeks invented the first alphabet in the world that had signs for vowels and consonants. The word 'alphabet' is made from the names of its first two letters. Use the signs to write your name or as a secret code with a friend. If you visit Greece, you will be able to read the shop signs. There have been changes to the pronunciation, but the letters are the same as they were nearly 3,000 years ago!

Greek Letter	Name	Sound	Greek Letter	Name	Sound
A α	alpha	J**a**ck	H η	eta	s**ee**
B β	beta	**B**illy	Θ θ	theta	Be**th**
Γ γ	gamma	**G**race	I ι	iota	K**i**t
Δ δ	delta	**D**aisy	K κ	kappa	Ni**ck**y
E ε	epsilon	**E**mily	Λ λ	lambda	Ji**ll**
Z ζ	zeta	**Z**oë	M μ	mu	**m**at

ΠΑΓΩΤΟ
ice cream

Greek Letter	Name	Sound	Greek Letter	Name	Sound
N ν	nu	**N**oddy	T τ	tau	s**t**op
Ξ ξ	xi	kic**ks**	Υ υ	upsilon	**U**na
O ο	omicron	B**o**b	Φ φ	phi	**Ph**il
Π π	pi	**p**ony	X χ	chi	**Kh**an
P ρ	rho	**R**ory	Ψ ψ	psi	li**ps**
Σ σ ς	sigma	**S**arah	Ω ω	omega	R**ow**an

TELEPHONE
WE'VE MADE NEW WORDS FROM ANCIENT GREEK ONES. 'TELE' MEANS 'FAR' AND 'PHONE' MEANS 'SOUND'. SEE IF YOU CAN FIND ANY MORE.

I'll see you later.

ANCIENT GREECE

Four thousand years ago, Europe's first civilizations began on the island of Crete and around the city of Mycenae. They were destroyed by earthquakes and war, but new cities took their place. The most powerful of these were Athens and Sparta.

2,600–1,400 BC
The first European civilization, called Minoan, began on the island of Crete.

1,400–1,100 BC
The Golden Age of Mycenae.

1,200 BC
Troy was besieged and destroyed by the Greeks.

THE GREEK MYTHS

The most famous Greek myth is the story of the warrior king, Odysseus, and his return home from Troy. The voyage took ten years. All his men were eaten by giants or killed by sea-monsters. Alone and dressed as a beggar, Odysseus defeated the last of his enemies and reclaimed his kingdom. Today the word 'odyssey' means a long journey full of adventures.

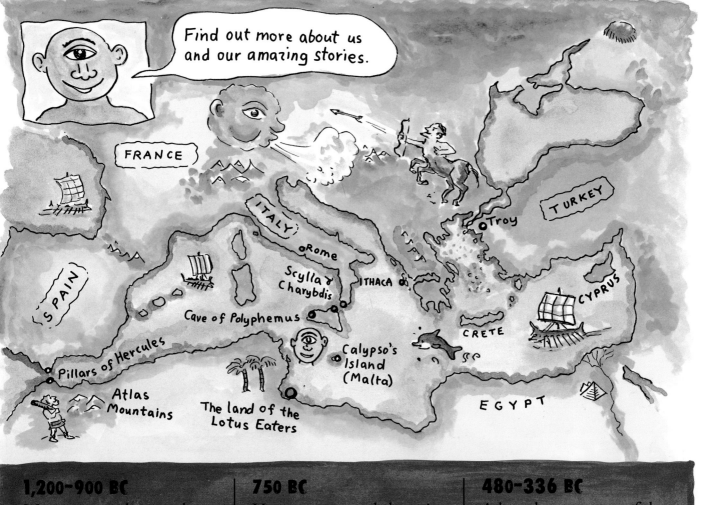

1,200–900 BC
Mycenae was destroyed in an age of war and destruction.

750 BC
Homer composed the epic story-poems, the *Iliad* and the *Odyssey*.

480–336 BC
Athens became powerful. This was the Classical Age.

HOW TO DRAW YOURSELF AS AN ANCIENT GREEK

Ancient Greek art is famous for its quality and beauty. The Greeks knew that their buildings and statues looked better when their design followed a rule called the golden mean. This was a rectangle drawn at a ratio of 1 to 1.618 and based on the measurements and shape of the human body.

YOU'LL NEED:
Pencil, paper, ruler, mirror, pencil rubber, paints or crayons.

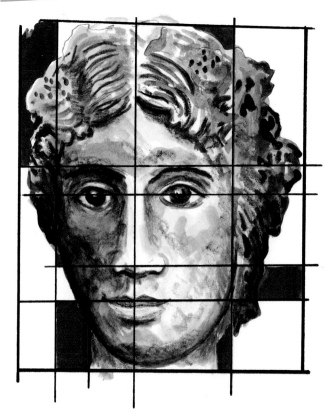

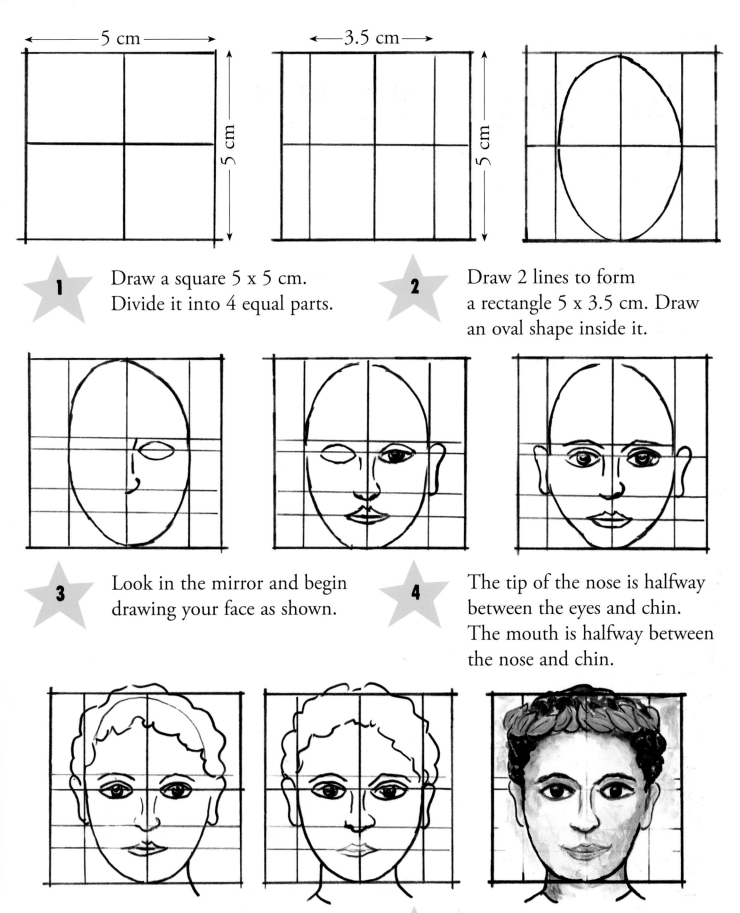

1 Draw a square 5 x 5 cm. Divide it into 4 equal parts.

2 Draw 2 lines to form a rectangle 5 x 3.5 cm. Draw an oval shape inside it.

3 Look in the mirror and begin drawing your face as shown.

4 The tip of the nose is halfway between the eyes and chin. The mouth is halfway between the nose and chin.

5 Rub out the guide lines and finish off with paints or crayons.

HOW TO MAKE THE HELMET OF HADES

This helmet belonged to Hades, the god of the underworld. Whoever wore it became invisible, so it was very handy for fighting monsters and giants. All the Ancient Greek heroes wanted a go with it. In the myths, Hades lent it to Perseus to help him kill the gorgon, Medusa.

TOP TIP - TOP TIP
Use a marker pen to draw in details around the eyes and mouth.

YOU'LL NEED:
2 x 2-litre plastic bottles, sandpaper, scissors, thin card, pencil, tracing paper, masking tape, ruler, marker pen, double-sided tape, acrylic paint and brushes.

If you do it right, when you put it on you should look like this:

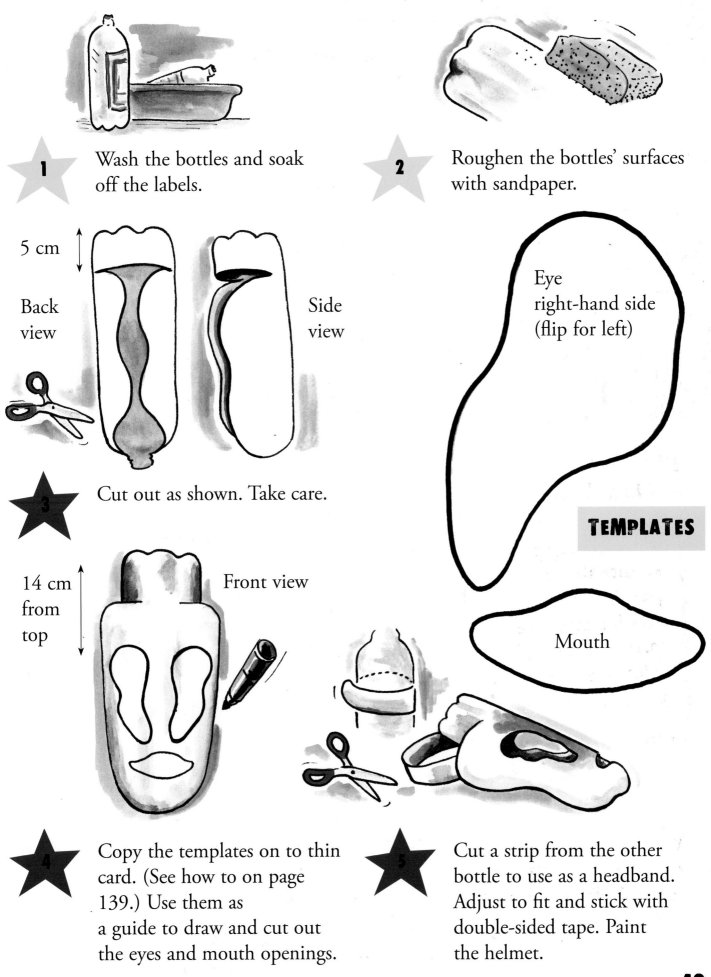

1 Wash the bottles and soak off the labels.

2 Roughen the bottles' surfaces with sandpaper.

5 cm

Back view

Side view

Cut out as shown. Take care.

3

Eye right-hand side (flip for left)

TEMPLATES

Mouth

14 cm from top

Front view

4 Copy the templates on to thin card. (See how to on page 139.) Use them as a guide to draw and cut out the eyes and mouth openings.

5 Cut a strip from the other bottle to use as a headband. Adjust to fit and stick with double-sided tape. Paint the helmet.

43

HOW TO MAKE PANDORA'S BOX

Pandora was the first woman. She was made from clay by the god Hephaestus in the shape of the beautiful goddess, Aphrodite. Zeus gave her a closed box and said it must never be opened. She really tried hard not to look inside, but just had to take a peep. Out flew every evil thing in the world. The only thing left was hope, stuck to the lid and fluttering like a tiny butterfly.

YOU'LL NEED:

Card (from a cereal box), thin paper, 15-cm elastic hair band, C6 size envelope, double-sided tape, scissors, pencil, craft knife, ruler, paints, brushes and felt-tips.

DO NOT OPEN!

Cut a piece of card 14 x 7 cm. Draw and score 4 lines and cut 4 small notches as shown.

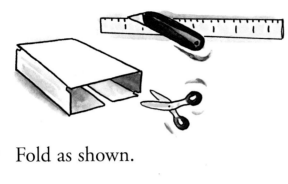

2 Fold as shown.

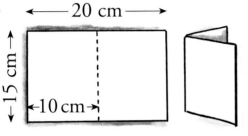

← 20 cm →

← 15 cm →

←10 cm→

Cut another piece of card 20 x 15 cm. Fold it in half and decorate the front.

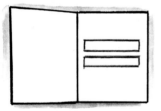

4 Draw 2 rectangles (7 x 2 cm) on the card, 5 cm from the top and 0.5 cm apart.

flattens this way

6 Stretch the elastic hair band around the notches. Make a small 'hope' and stick it to the top. Cut some small nasties from thin paper and place on top. Press and hold flat.

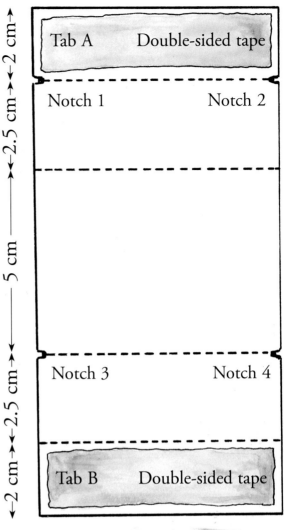

← 2 cm → ← 2.5 cm → ← 5 cm → ← 2.5 cm → ← 2 cm →

Tab A	Double-sided tape
Notch 1	Notch 2
Notch 3	Notch 4
Tab B	Double-sided tape

5 Carefully stick tabs A and B to the rectangles with double-sided tape.

7 Carefully close the card and place in the envelope, open side first. When opened the little nasties will be flung out.

HOW TO MAKE A WINNER'S OLIVE WREATH

The first Olympic Games were held in Greece nearly 2,800 years ago. The winners were given a wreath to wear, made from olive leaves. The Ancient Greeks stopped all fighting while the games were on. An olive branch is still the symbol of peace today.

YOU'LL NEED:

Thick green paper at least 63 cm wide, a small piece of card, tracing paper, masking tape, scissors, ruler, pencil, glue, paints and brushes and/or metallic pens.

TOP TIP – TOP TIP

Make more leaves by cutting through several layers of paper at once.

63 cm

5 cm

TEMPLATE

1 Cut a piece of paper 5 x 63 cm and fold it in half.

2 Slide one end into the other until it fits your head and glue.

3 Copy the template on to the card (see the instructions on page 139) and cut it out.

4 Draw round the shape on the green paper and cut it out to make a leaf. Make lots more.

5 Fold the leaves in half. Glue the stalks into the headband. Don't make them look too neat.

6 You can paint them if you like and let them dry. Some wreaths were made of gold or silver.

Symbols from the Myths

All great stories need a great set of characters. The Greek myths had a fabulous line-up. Have a look at some of the myths, then try making up your own stories using some of these symbols.

Helmet

Sword

Helmets and swords often had magical powers.

Shield

The goddess Athene gave Perseus a shield polished like a mirror. He looked at the gorgon, Medusa, through it and that stopped him being turned to stone.

Arrow

Eros, the cheeky little god of love, shot people with gold-tipped arrows and they fell in love.

Dolphin

Jason and the Argonauts sailed to the very edge of the world in search of the Golden Fleece.

Dolphins guided ships and took messages for the gods.

Pegasus, the flying horse. A useful friend in an emergency.

Beautiful Princess

Princess Ariadne helped Theseus escape from the labyrinth after he killed the Minotaur.

Thunderbolt of Zeus

Doric Column

Ionic Column

Corinthian Column

Scary Monster

One of the best known monsters was the Minotaur. He had the head of a bull and the body of a man – the first cowboy perhaps?

Vases were painted with scenes from the myths.

Brave Warrior

He was always ready to fight monsters and giants.

49

MIDDLE AGES ACTIVITIES
HOW TO MAKE A CROWN

Kings and queens were very powerful people in the Middle Ages. They were always plotting and fighting over who should wear the crown, so here is one for each of them.

YOU'LL NEED:

2 pieces of paper 62 x 10 cm, thin card, scissors, ruler, pencil, tracing paper, masking tape, glue, paints and/or metallic pens.

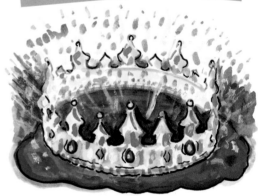

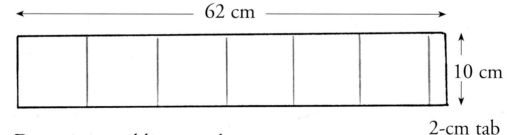

62 cm

10 cm

2-cm tab

1 Draw six pencil lines on the paper 10 cm apart.

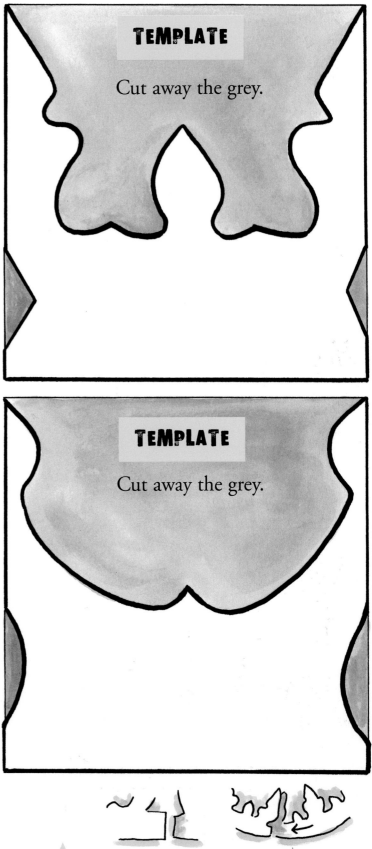

TEMPLATE

Cut away the grey.

⭐ **2** Fold the paper along these lines.

⭐ **3** Copy the templates on to the card (using the instructions on page 139). Cut them out.

TEMPLATE

Cut away the grey.

⭐ **4** Use them to draw the crown outlines on to the paper.

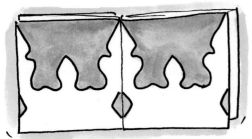

⭐ **5** Cut out the outlines as shown. If the paper is too thick to cut, open it out and draw two outlines to cut round.

⭐ **6** Fit to your head and glue the ends together. Decorate with paints and/or pens.

HOW TO BUILD YOUR OWN FOLD-UP CASTLE

Now you have a crown, you need a castle to protect it. Thousands of castles were built all across Europe during the Middle Ages. Every ruler wanted theirs to be the biggest and the best with all the latest defences. Prague Castle in the Czech Republic and Windsor Castle in England are two of the biggest still in one piece.

YOU'LL NEED:

Large cardboard packing box (from a chair or fridge), Velcro self-adhesive tape, PVA glue, craft knife, scissors, ruler, marker pen, paints and brushes.

TOP TIP - TOP TIP

Cut some slits in the walls to keep a look-out for approaching enemy armies.

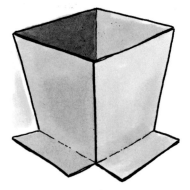

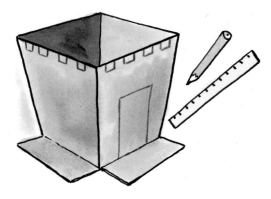

★ Cut off the flaps except for two adjoining flaps at the bottom of the box. (Keep the cut-offs.)

2 Mark out battlements and a drawbridge (on a side with a flap).

★ Carefully cut them out, leaving the bottom of the drawbridge to form a hinge. Fold the bottom flaps under the box.

4 Glue a cut-off flap inside the top of the opening. Glue another to the inside of the drawbridge door so you can pull it shut.

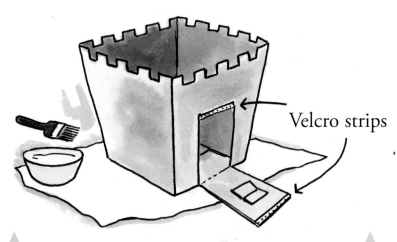

Velcro strips

5 Paint the whole box with PVA diluted with three times the amount of water and allow it to dry. Stick Velcro where shown.

6 Paint to look like stone and wood. Give a final coat of diluted PVA for extra strength. The castle will fold flat to store.

HOW TO MAKE A POCKET SIEGE ENGINE

Before the invention of gunpowder, fearsome machines called trebuchets were used to attack castles. Anything from huge rocks, dead horses and even the occasional foreign ambassador could be flung over the castle walls.

YOU'LL NEED:

2 oblong plastic ice-cream tub lids (1-litre size), sticky tape, double-sided tape, scissors, ruler, craft knife, fine marker pen, some not very important homework for ammunition.

A FARMER IN ENGLAND HAS BUILT HIS OWN FULL-SIZE MEDIEVAL SIEGE ENGINE. IT CAN FLING A PIANO 125 METRES. IN TEXAS, AN ENGINEER AND AN ARTIST BUILT A MODEL FOR THROWING '57 BUICKS.

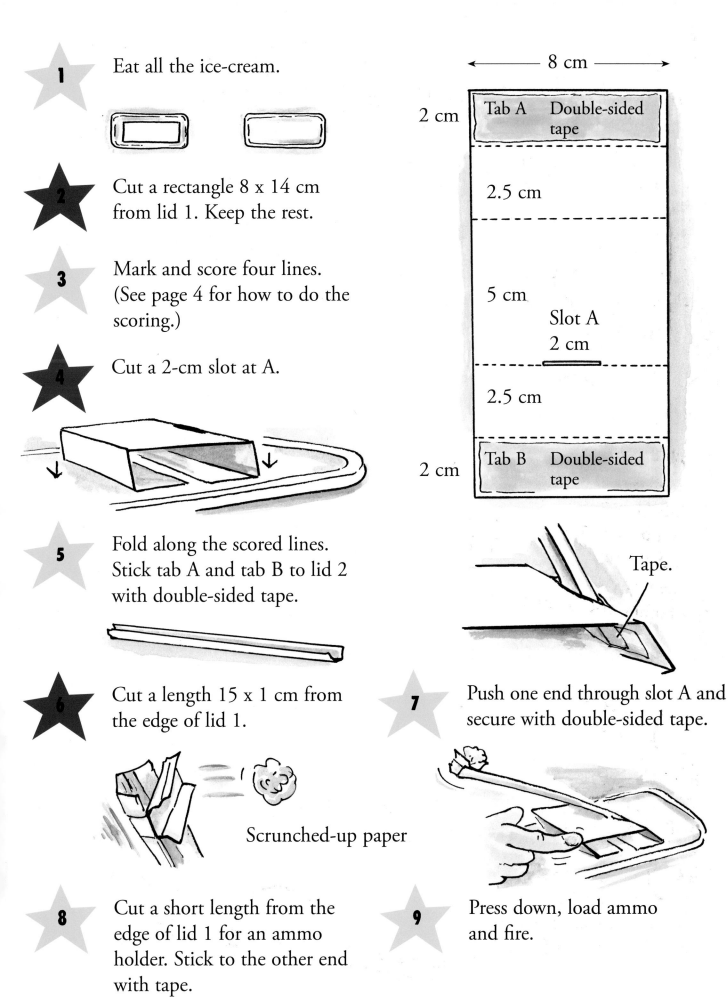

1 Eat all the ice-cream.

2 Cut a rectangle 8 x 14 cm from lid 1. Keep the rest.

3 Mark and score four lines. (See page 4 for how to do the scoring.)

4 Cut a 2-cm slot at A.

5 Fold along the scored lines. Stick tab A and tab B to lid 2 with double-sided tape.

6 Cut a length 15 x 1 cm from the edge of lid 1.

Scrunched-up paper

7 Push one end through slot A and secure with double-sided tape.

Tape.

8 Cut a short length from the edge of lid 1 for an ammo holder. Stick to the other end with tape.

9 Press down, load ammo and fire.

8 cm

2 cm Tab A   Double-sided tape

2.5 cm

5 cm
Slot A
2 cm

2.5 cm

2 cm Tab B   Double-sided tape

HOW TO MAKE A MAYPOLE

May Day was a very important festival in the Middle Ages. It celebrated the end of winter and the flowering of spring. In many countries in Europe there was feasting and games and dancing round the maypole. A May queen was chosen and crowned with a garland of wild flowers.

YOU'LL NEED:

1 x 1-litre screw-top drink carton, 10-cm round plastic lid, strong paper 45 x 12 cm, 7 different-coloured ribbons 40 cm long, scissors, coloured sticky tape, ruler, glue, pencil, scraps of green material.

TOP TIP - TOP TIP

Cut out some small paper flowers and stick them to the maypole.

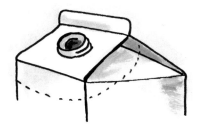

1 Remove the screwcap and open out the top of the carton.

2 Draw a circle around the spout, then cut it out.

3 Glue it to the plastic lid.

4 Knot the ribbons together and glue to one corner of the paper.

5 Coil and twist the paper, then trim the end.

6 Adjust the width and height of the paper tube by pulling it gently. Glue the end inside the spout. Hold until dry.

7 Use colored adhesive tape to strengthen and decorate your maypole.

8 Glue scraps of green fabric over the base.

HOW TO SAY IT WITH FLOWERS

People have always loved flowers and each one has its own meaning. In the Middle Ages a knight could give his sweetheart certain flowers to show his love for her. She could then reply appropriately. It was very handy if you were shy or just wanted to say 'get lost'!

YOU'LL NEED:
Paper, small piece of card, pencil, tracing paper, masking tape, scissors, glue, compass, wire bag ties, paints and brushes.

TOP TIP – TOP TIP
Cut out several petals at a time by drawing on folded paper.

1 Copy the templates on to the card (see the instructions on page 139). Cut them out.

Petal

Centre

2 Draw round the templates on to the paper to make five petals and one centre. Cut them out.

3 Paint the petals red on both sides. Paint the centre gold.

4 Arrange the petals one over the other like this and glue together.

5 Make two holes with the compass through the middle.

6 Thread through the bag tie and twist it together.

Red rose
True love
Pink rose
secret love

7 Glue on the gold centre.

Find out the meanings of some more flowers.

59

MAP OF EUROPE

in the Middle Ages

1066
The Battle of Hastings.
The Normans conquer
England.

1215
King John of England signs
the Magna Carta promising
that laws will be good
and fair.

1300
First use of cannons and
gunpowder in Europe.

1347-49
The Black Death wipes out a third of Europe's population.

1447
Printing with moveable type invented in Germany.

1492
Columbus discovers America.

HOW TO MAKE A MEDIEVAL PUDDING

Choosing what to have for pudding was a different matter in the olden days. It wasn't as easy as looking in the freezer. Fruits, especially soft berries, were difficult to store and had to be freshly picked when they were in season.

Yes we have no chocolate, potatoes, or tomatoes, but I've made a lovely fruit crisp!

MUCH OF OUR FAVOURITE FOOD WAS UNKNOWN IN EUROPE UNTIL COLUMBUS DISCOVERED AMERICA IN 1492. THANKS CHRIS.

62

⭐ **1** Wash your hands. Open the packets of fruit and pour the juice into the small jug.

⭐ **2** Put the fruit into the ovenproof dish. Drizzle about 3 heaped tablespoons of honey over it.

⭐ **3** Remove the crusts and break the bread into chunks. Chop in the food processor to make large breadcrumbs.

⭐ **4** Put them into the large bowl and add the nuts (if using). Mix together.

⭐ **5** Spread them over the fruit. Bake in a moderate oven for 20-25 minutes.

⭐ **6** Gently heat the juice. Add about 1 heaped tablespoon of honey and serve with the pudding.

63

HOW TO PLAY THREE MEN'S MERELS

Merels is one of the oldest games in the world still played today. It was very popular in the Middle Ages. Merel boards have been found carved in the stones of Europe's great cathedrals. There are several versions. Three men's merels is the simplest. It's really good. Learn to play this using the board on the opposite page, then you can try the harder one, nine men's merels.

YOU'LL NEED:
2 sets of 3 counters and someone to play with.

TOP TIP – TOP TIP
Coloured bottle tops make really good counters.

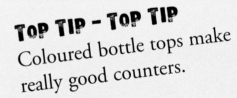

1 Decide who goes first. Each player has three counters.

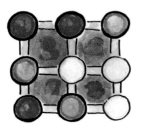

2 Take turns to place a counter on a blank spot until all six are used up.

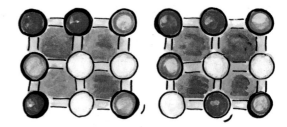

3 Move one of your counters to a free spot next to it.

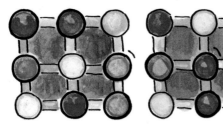

4 The aim is to get your three counters in a row called a mill. They can go across, up or down, but not diagonally.

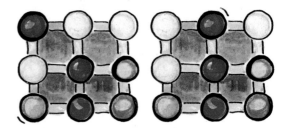

5 You have won when you get a mill or the other player cannot move.

HOW TO DRAW AN ILLUMINATED LETTER

Before the invention of printing, every book was written and drawn by hand. Some books took years to finish and were so valuable that they had to be chained up. Each page began with a large beautifully decorated capital letter.

I'm just dotting the **i**s, crossing the **t**s and adding a large sea serpent to each **S**. I'll be about two years.

YOU'LL NEED:

Paper, graph paper, pencil, ruler, compass, black, coloured and metallic pens, paints and brushes, scissors, glue.

TOP TIP – TOP TIP

Try writing your initials like this.

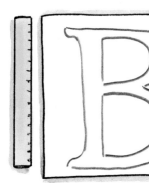

1 Draw a big outline of your letter in pencil on graph paper. Use the ruler and compass.

2 Add flowers or animals or funny faces.

3 Paint in the colours and allow to dry. If you like, use your metallic pens too.

4 Go over the outlines in black pen. Cut out the square and stick to your paper to continue your writing.

HOW TO MAKE A COAT OF ARMS

Coats of arms were invented in the Middle Ages. Each knight had their own special design. They were the medieval equivalent of today's logos and brand names. Use the templates on page 142 and the examples on the following pages to make your own. Look up your name on the internet, your family may have one already.

YOU'LL NEED:
Paper or thin card, pencil, coloured pens, paints and brushes, ruler, stencils.

HERALDIC PAINT BOX
These were the colours used in coats of arms. They had to be bright and easy to see in battle.

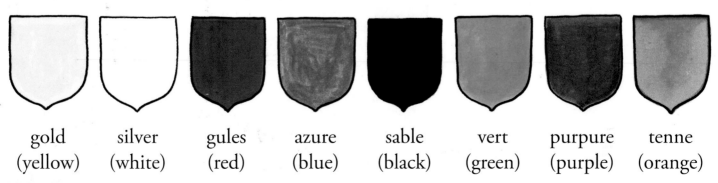

| gold (yellow) | silver (white) | gules (red) | azure (blue) | sable (black) | vert (green) | purpure (purple) | tenne (orange) |

sword

dragon

lion

heart

star

lozenge

cross

roundel

crescent

bell

fleur-de-lis

shield

sheaf

conch shell

shamrock

sun

castle

crown

HOW TO CREATE AN HERALDIC MONSTER

The knights used pictures of fierce animals like lions, leopards and dragons on their shields. They also made up animals. A Gryphon had the head and wings of an eagle and the body of a lion. Why not make up your own? Here are two examples.

Guineafish

Caterigar

Unicorn

Salamander

Gryphon

70

Copy the shield template on to paper
or card (see the instructions on page 139).
Use the stencils to design your
own coat of arms. Then try creating a logo
with simple pictures of your favourite
things: perhaps a dolphin, a mobile
phone or a huge chocolate
cake with cherries
on top.

TEMPLATE

PREHISTORIC ACTIVITIES
HOW TO MAKE YOUR OWN
PLANET EARTH

The world didn't always look as it does today. Once, there was just one piece of land. Over millions of years this huge mass, called Pangaea, split apart to form Laurasia and Gondwana. It continued to break up and is still doing so today. If you look on an atlas you can see which countries might once have been joined together.

YOU'LL NEED:

Large round balloon, old magazines and newspapers, paper paste (see page 4 for instructions), plastic mixing bowl, PVA glue, paints and brushes, string, coathanger.

33 million years ago, palm trees grew in Antarctica.

Animals could walk across the land before it split up.

ASIA
NORTH AMERICA
EUROPE
SOUTH AMERICA
AFRICA
ARABIA
INDIA
ANTARCTICA
AUSTRALIA

1 Mix up some paper paste. Blow up the balloon and tie the end with string.

2 Tear the paper into small strips. Make one pile of black and white and one of coloured strips.

3 Dip the strips in the paste and cover the balloon.

4 Use black and white strips for one layer and coloured for the next. This will keep the thickness even.

5 You'll need about 10 layers for a good strong Earth's crust. Hang up to dry.

6 Tear some more newsprint into small pieces and mix them with the paste into a pulp. Use this to mould islands, mountains and volcanoes.

7 Hang up to dry overnight. Paint in forests and oceans, rivers and icebergs. Finish off with PVA diluted 1:3 to make it bright and waterproof.

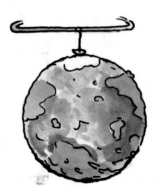

HOW TO FIND FOSSILS

You might not find a rare dinosaur, but fossil hunting is very exciting. Even a small find is rewarding. Look in places like beaches, cliffs, quarries and ploughed fields. Some very good ones can be found on gravel paths and drives. So many wonders of the prehistoric past would be lost to us without them.

MARVELLOUS MARY

In 1811 Mary Anning, aged only 12, found the first complete ichthyosaur. She called it her crocodile. A few years later she found a plesiosaur and a pterosaur. She was called 'the cleverest fossilist the world has ever known'.

Nice croccy!

YOU'LL NEED:

(You may not need all of these.) A strong bag, plastic bags, notebook, pen, crayons, strong thin paper, pencil, masking tape, small trowel or knife, magnifying glass, suitable clothes, old rag, PVA glue, camera.

Fossils are formed when water seeps into the hard parts of a living creature that has died. Minerals in the water gradually replace the shape with stone.

1 Ask a grown-up to go with you. They'll show you safe places and they're handy for carrying heavy bags.

2 Always ask permission if you're going on to privately owned land.

3 Look out for: shells, bones, teeth, eggs, plants, wood, footprints and funny-shaped stones. They may be coprolites – fossilized poo, well past its smell-by date!

4 Bag them and tag them. Find their names in a book or on a website, or visit a museum.

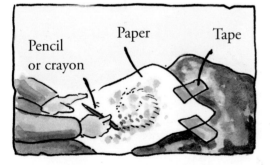

5 Note where you found them. Make a rubbing or take a photo of anything embedded in rock.

6 Once home, soak them in clean water. Clean and dry with a rag. Paint with a coat of PVA glue to protect them and keep them bright.

HOW TO MAKE LAVA LOLLIES

Many millions of years ago, even before there were any oceans, the Earth was full of volcanoes. When they erupted, rocks, so hot they were liquid, shot out. The red hot stream that oozed down the volcano sides, we call lava.

KITCHENWARE YOU'LL NEED:
Sharp knife, plate, teaspoon.

INGREDIENTS YOU'LL NEED:
ice-cream (any flavour), cornets, strawberry sauce topping at room temperature.

RADIO METRIC DATING AS SOON AS ROCK IS FORMED, IT STARTS TO DECAY (BREAK DOWN) AT A STEADY RATE. MEASURING THIS TELLS US HOW OLD THE ROCK IS.

 1 First, wash your hands.

 2 Fill about one third of a cone with strawberry sauce.

 3 Pack with ice-cream, rounding off the top.

 Turn over on to plate and cut off the top 3 cm of the cone.

 5 Push gently down and watch the lava flow!

Don't eat too many or you might erupt!

HOW TO DRAW-A-SAUR

It's a great shame we can't jump back in time and watch the dinosaurs – from a safe distance, of course. You'd have seen all shapes and sizes. Try these features to make your own monster: frilly necks, spiky tails, horns, humps, sharp claws, and big jaws with an 'I'm going to eat you' smile. But none, it seems, had big, sticky-out ears. I wonder why?

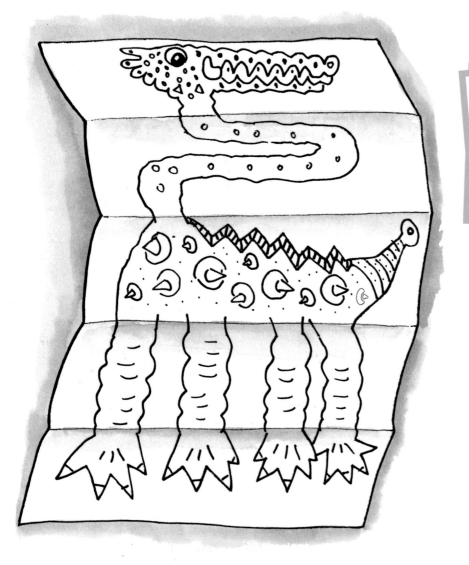

YOU'LL NEED:
Your friends each with an A4 piece of paper, pencils, pens, felt-tips.

NOBODY IS SURE WHAT COLOUR DINOSAURS WERE. THEY MAY HAVE BEEN LIKE TODAY'S REPTILES.

1 Keep your drawings secret and let your imagination go.

2 Draw a dinosaur head. Fold the paper backwards leaving two small lines to show the next person where to continue drawing.

3 Pass it to the person on your left for them to draw a neck. Carry on like this and draw in this order: a head, a neck, a body and tail, legs, feet.

TOP TIP - TOP TIP

Often, dinosaurs are named after the place they are found in or the person who found them, so give yours a suitable name!

4 Then unfold to reveal the latest dinosaur discovery.

HOW TO MAKE A FINGERSAUR

Imagine your finger as the long neck of a plant-eating dinosaur! Make the frill and turn it into a triceratops. Put one on each finger and have a whole dinosaur family.

TRICERATOPS MEANS THREE-HORNED FACE.

YOU'LL NEED:

For the dinosaur:
face paints.
For the triceratops:
paper, tracing paper, masking tape, scissors, pencil, paints and brushes or crayons, sticky tape.

Have you got a sore finger?

No, it's a fingersaur!

chomp chomp

DINOSAUR

 1 Paint your hand and a little face on your index finger.

2 With your thumb and middle finger as the legs, pull your sleeve down and let your dinosaur go for a walk.

TRICERATOPS

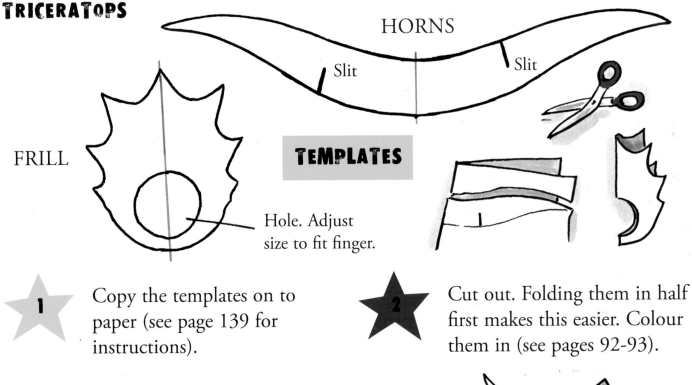

HORNS

Slit

Slit

FRILL

TEMPLATES

Hole. Adjust size to fit finger.

1 Copy the templates on to paper (see page 139 for instructions).

2 Cut out. Folding them in half first makes this easier. Colour them in (see pages 92-93).

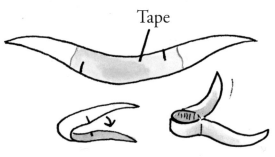

Tape

3 Cut the slits in the horns as shown. Put sticky tape on the back first to stop them tearing. Slot one into the other.

4 Put the frill on first, then the horns. Paint an extra horn on your finger face to make a 'tri' ceratops.

PREHISTORIC DISCOVERIES

New discoveries are being made all the time. It is surprising how many are made by children!

Rocky Mountains, Canada.
In the Burgess Shale, in the Yoho National Park, 505-million-year-old fossils found. One was of our oldest known ancestors.

Lascaux, France.
Amazing cave paintings found in 1940.

Rio Puerco, Albuquerque, USA.
A three-year-old boy found a fossilized eggshell. It was the oldest evidence of an egg-laying, meat-eating dinosaur.

Dad!

Plaza Huincul, Patagonia.
Argentinasaurus found in the 1990s. The biggest dinosaur discovered so far. It was as big as a herd of elephants.

360-300 MYA
First reptiles appeared.

208-146 MYA
Jurassic period. Many dinosaurs lived.

65 MYA
Many living things died out, including the dinosaurs.

mya stands for million years ago.

82

Stonehenge, UK.
Stone Age temple to the Sun.

South-east Belgium.
In 1878, coalminers found 31 iguanodon.

Siberia.
Woolly mammoth found in a 23-tonne block of ice. Almost perfectly preserved, it still had its fur and stomach contents.

Brrrr!

Liaoning Province, North-east China.
Fossils found of a four-winged dinosaur with feathers on its front and back limbs.

Comoro Islands, Indian Ocean.
Coelacanths alive and well.

What's the fuss?

Hadar, Ethiopia.
Bones of a female hominid found. The first evidence that an ape-like creature stood up and walked on two legs. She was named Lucy after the Beatles' song.

I'm not that old, whacker!

65 MYA – NOW
The Age of the Mammals.

7 MYA
First hominid (ancestor of modern man).

10,000 YEARS AGO
Last Ice Age ended.

THE STONE AGE

Prehistoric people lived in caves and wore animal skins. They used sharp stones called flints as tools and hunted fierce wild beasts like mammoths for food. The children were taught to hunt and collect nuts and berries. Beautiful pictures of animals have been found inside the caves.

MAMMOTHS WERE LIKE VERY HAIRY ELEPHANTS WITH ENORMOUS TUSKS.

HOW TO MAKE A FIERCE POP-UP!

Smilodon, the sabre-tooth tiger, was more like a modern-day lion than a tiger. Too heavy to run for a long time, it waited until its prey came near, then pounced. One bite with those huge fangs and dinner was served.

YOU'LL NEED:
2 sheets of card 24 x 12 cm, pencil, tracing paper, masking tape, scissors, ruler, glue, paints and felt-tips.

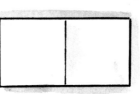

Happy Grrrthday!

1 Divide each piece of card in half and score (see instructions on page 4).

2 Copy tiger templates on to one card (see instructions on page 139).

3 Cut round the bold outlines. Score and fold along the blue lines.

4 Colour in your tiger face.

CARD 1 24 x 12 cm

TIGER TEMPLATES

Tab A

Tab C

Tab D

Tab B

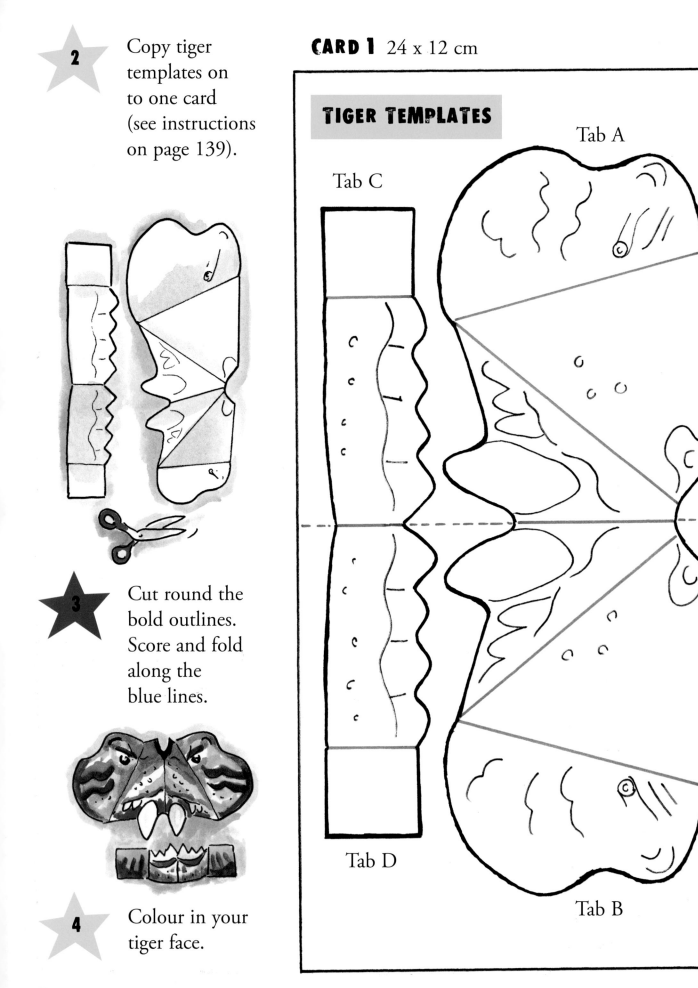

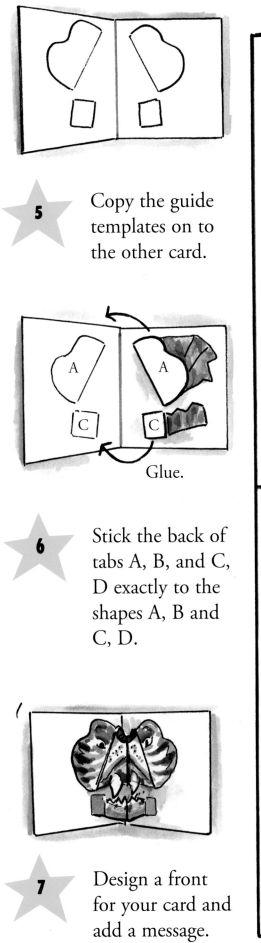

5 Copy the guide templates on to the other card.

Glue.

6 Stick the back of tabs A, B, and C, D exactly to the shapes A, B and C, D.

7 Design a front for your card and add a message.

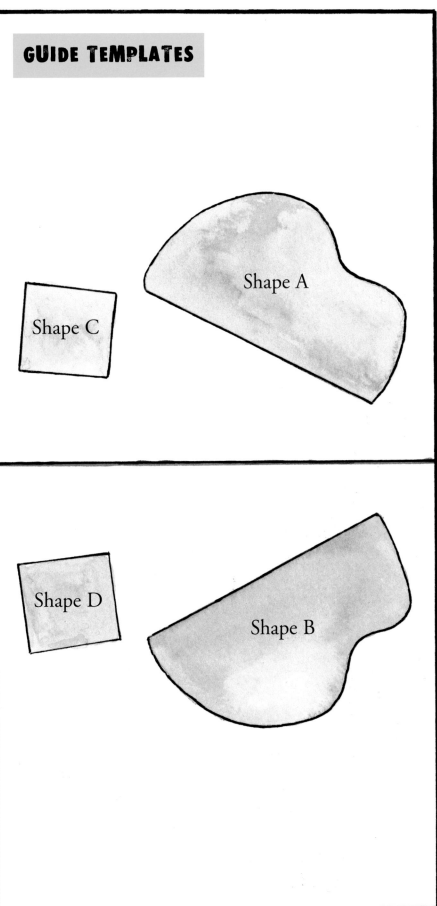

GUIDE TEMPLATES

Shape C

Shape A

Shape D

Shape B

87

HOW TO BE A CAVEMAN

The Neanderthals were Stone Age people who lived in Europe during the last Ice Age between 200,000 and 30,000 years ago. Woolly rhinos roamed the valleys, the sea froze, and knowing how to light a fire became a matter of life or death.

YOU'LL NEED:
3 x 2-litre clear plastic drinks bottles (labels removed), sandpaper/block, scissors, craft knife, marker pen, ruler, acrylic paints and brushes, double-sided tape, glue, 12 x 26 cm bubble plastic.

Everything's been invented already... fire, axes, sabre-tooth tiger trousers...

1 Wash and roughen the bottles' surfaces with sandpaper.

88

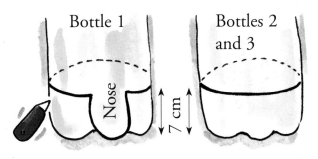

Bottle 1   Bottles 2 and 3

Nose

7 cm

⭐ **2** Mark as shown and cut. Use a craft knife for the nose on bottle 1.

⭐ **3** Cut the tops off all bottles and cut down the back. Open them out.

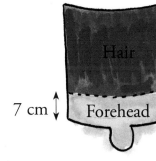

Hair

7 cm   Forehead

⭐ **4** On all bottles mark a guide line and paint as shown.

⭐ **5** When dry, cut narrow strips for hair.

Front view

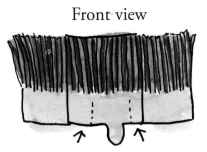

Back view

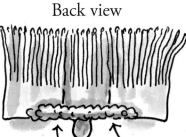

⭐ **6** Overlap and fix together with double-sided tape.

⭐ **7** Glue rolled-up bubble plastic inside forehead.

⭐ **8** Pull some through to the front and paint like eyebrows.

⭐ **9** Fit to your head. Join at the back with double-sided tape. See if you can invent the wheel.

89

MONSTER MYSTERIES

Scientists can tell us incredible things about the past, but they don't know everything. There are lots of unexplained mysteries. The world is full of things yet to be discovered and new finds force us to rearrange the jigsaw pieces of the past. Have all the prehistoric creatures died out? Do we know everything that lives on Earth?

CSI CSI CSI CSI CSI

CRYPTO SCIENCE INVESTIGATION

BIGFOOT
Hundreds of people have reported seeing creatures like primitive ape men in North America. They were known to Native Americans as Sasquatch. Footprints have been found and photographed, but we have no absolute proof of Bigfoot.

Can you see what it is yeti?

YETI
Also called the Abominable Snowman. Very similar to Bigfoot but seen very high up in the mountains in Tibet where few people ever go.

LOCH NESS MONSTER
Many people insist they've seen a strange creature in Loch Ness in Scotland. It's got a long neck and fits the description of a plesiosaur.

ITHOUGHTISAURUS
← TOURIST OFFICE

See yer later, big mon!

THE LATEST ON THE EARLIEST

In 2002 a fossil was found in China of a flying dinosaur. It was 76 cm long and 120 million years old. It had four wings and was covered with feathers. It may prove a link between dinosaurs and birds.

Mummy!

'IT WAS THIS BIG'

The study of creatures people say they have seen but have no definite proof of is called cryptozoology.

COELACANTHS

More ancient than the dinosaurs, these fish were thought to have died out 80 million years ago. So imagine how amazed scientists were when one was found in fishermen's nets in 1938. They live in very deep water off the coast of South Africa under the close watch of conservationists.

We never had those newfangled dinosaur thingies when I was a nipper.

DINOSAUR I.D.

We humans are the newcomers on Earth. Scientists say simple life began 550 million years ago. As the Earth's climate changed, life adapted to take advantage of the new conditions. Dinosaurs thrived wonderfully during three main periods of history: the Triassic (250 to 208 mya), the Jurassic (208 to 146 mya) and the Cretaceous (146 to 65 mya). Then for some reason they just died out ... or did they? See pages 90–91.

TYRANNOSAURUS CRETACEOUS
A truly terrifying dinosaur. Huge head, razor sharp teeth, massive legs and tail. Why the ridiculously short arms? Probably no one dared ask.

PARASAUROLOPHUS CRETACEOUS
A duck-billed dinosaur. Could have made sounds through the bony crest on its head. What sweet music!

STEGOSAURUS JURASSIC
Big plates along its top, spikes on its tail and a tiny little brain the size of a walnut. His mummy still loved him.

PTEROSAUR
CRETACEOUS
Pterosaur is a name given
to flying reptiles. The
pteranodon was a large
pterosaur. It had a 7-metre
wingspan and a body the
size of a goose.

CETIOSAURUS JURASSIC
Unbelievably huge. A solid backbone
made it even heavier. Stones in its
stomach ground up the veggie dinners
of this early plant-eater.

TRICERATOPS CRETACEOUS
Had a beaky mouth like a parrot
to help eat tough vegetation.
Who's a pretty polly then?

ANKYLOSAURUS CRETACEOUS
As big as an army tank and covered
in bony spikes. Wagged its tail at its
enemies and knocked them flying.

VELOCIRAPTOR CRETACEOUS
Sharp teeth and claws like scythes.
Probably thought a minute before
scratching that itch!

COELOPHYSIS TRIASSIC
These lizard-like creatures were possibly
the very first dinosaurs on the Earth.

ROMAN ACTIVITIES
HOW TO MAKE A TABULA

Children learned to write using a wax tablet called a **tabula**. This was a wooden board covered with a thin layer of beeswax. The letters were scratched on the wax surface with a sharp stick called a **stylus**. They were rubbed out by smoothing over them with the round end of the stylus, leaving the tablet fresh and ready to use again.

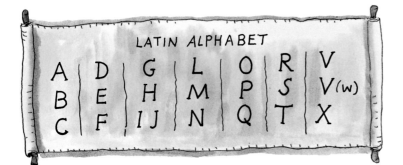

LATIN ALPHABET

A D G L O R V
B E H M P S V(w)
C F IJ N Q T X

YOU'LL NEED:
Corrugated cardboard, rolling-pin, plasticine, craft knife, scissors, glue, ruler, pencil, old ballpoint pen, paints and brushes.

GRAFFITI
WRITING ON WALLS ISN'T NEW. THE ROMANS DID IT A LOT, OFTEN USING A CHISEL!

SPARTACVS INNOCENS EST VERITATE
(Spartacus is innocent, OK!)

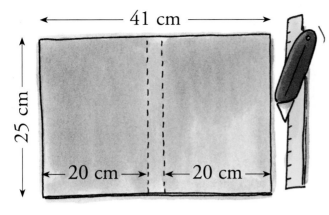

1 Cut out a rectangle of corrugated cardboard.

2 Use the scissors to score two lines down the centre 1 cm apart. Fold to make a spine.

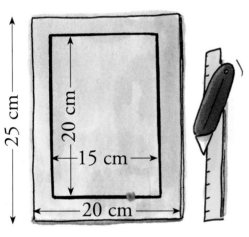

3 Cut out another cardboard rectangle. Cut out the centre to form a frame.

4 Glue this to the right-hand side of the first rectangle.

5 Roll some plasticine flat and fill the frame with it.

6 Decorate the front of the **tabula** using the templates on page 144 and mosaics on pages 98-99. Use the old ballpoint pen as a **stylus**. Rub out with the plastic cap.

HOW TO MAKE AN ABACUS

Roman numbers were based on the hand. One finger was held up for 1 and one hand for 5, written as the letter V. Two hands were 10, written as two Vs, like this V/\. This became the letter X. Later other letters were used for bigger numbers: L=50 C=100 D=500 M=1,000.

This system made doing sums really hard, so the Romans used a simple counting board called an **abacus** with small stones as hundreds, tens and units.

YOU'LL NEED:
Thin card, 27 bottle tops or coins, ruler, pencil, glue and scissors.

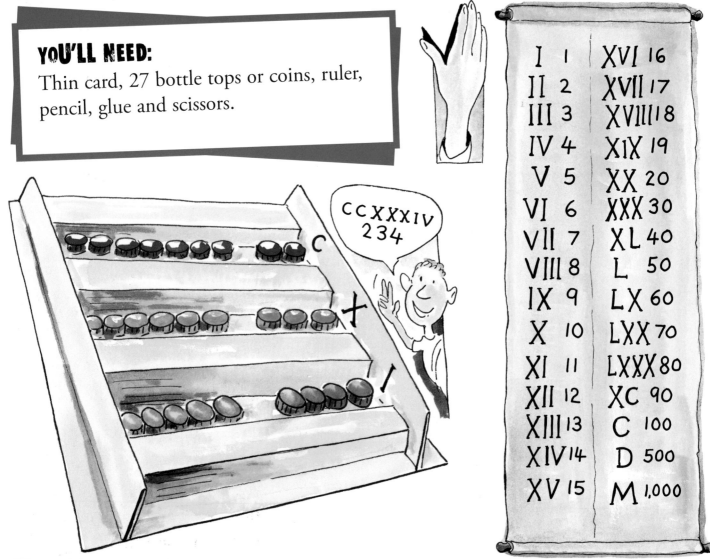

CCXXXIV 234

I	1	XVI	16
II	2	XVII	17
III	3	XVIII	18
IV	4	XIX	19
V	5	XX	20
VI	6	XXX	30
VII	7	XL	40
VIII	8	L	50
IX	9	LX	60
X	10	LXX	70
XI	11	LXXX	80
XII	12	XC	90
XIII	13	C	100
XIV	14	D	500
XV	15	M	1,000

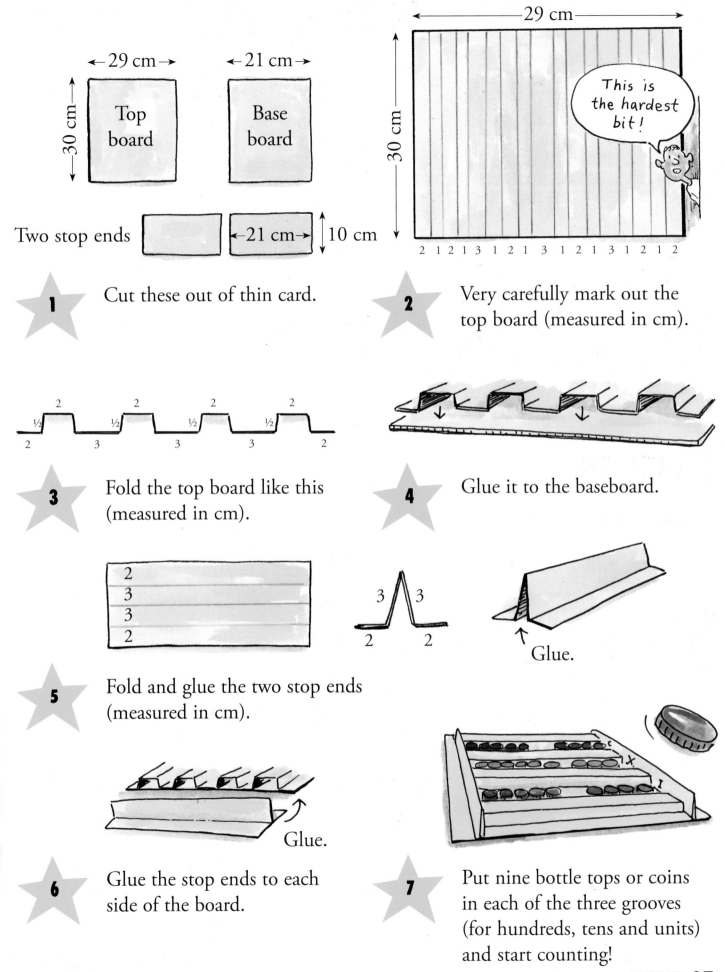

← 29 cm →   ← 21 cm →

30 cm   Top board   Base board

Two stop ends   ← 21 cm → 10 cm

← 29 cm →

30 cm

2 1 2 1 3 1 2 1 3 1 2 1 3 1 2 1 2

This is the hardest bit!

1 Cut these out of thin card.

2 Very carefully mark out the top board (measured in cm).

2   2   2   2
½   ½   ½   ½
2   3   3   3   2

3 Fold the top board like this (measured in cm).

4 Glue it to the baseboard.

2
3
3
2

3   3
2   2

Glue.

5 Fold and glue the two stop ends (measured in cm).

Glue.

6 Glue the stop ends to each side of the board.

7 Put nine bottle tops or coins in each of the three grooves (for hundreds, tens and units) and start counting!

HOW TO MAKE A MOSAIC

Roman mosaics are famous. They are pictures made up of thousands of tiny pieces of coloured stone or tile fixed in cement. They were used to decorate the floors of Roman villas. You can see them in museums all over the world.

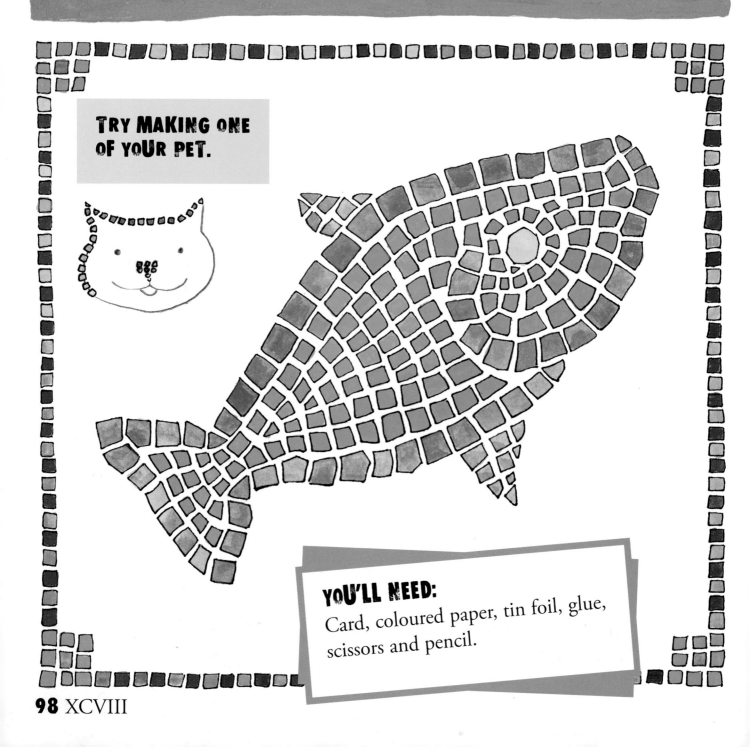

TRY MAKING ONE OF YOUR PET.

YOU'LL NEED:
Card, coloured paper, tin foil, glue, scissors and pencil.

1 Glue coloured paper and tin foil on to pieces of card.

2 Then cut the card into small shapes like this.

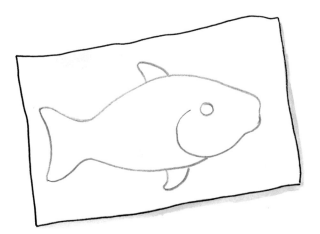

3 Draw an outline of your design on a piece of paper or card.

TOP TIP - TOP TIP
Use empty yogurt pots to store the coloured shapes.

4 Glue the small shapes on to your design. You can trim them to fit.

HOW TO MAKE A ROMAN BORDER

Beautiful mosaics were often surrounded by a black and white border. The Romans used simple shapes and repeated them to make patterns. They were always worked out first on a grid. Squared paper makes this easy. Have a look at the ideas on the page opposite. You could try them or experiment and make up your own designs. Beware, sometimes the squares make your eyes go funny!

YOU'LL NEED:
Squared paper, black felt-tips, black and white paint and brushes or crayons, ruler and pencil.

TOP TIP – TOP TIP
Copy the design by marking the squares in pencil with a 'b' for black. These will be hidden when you paint over them.

1. Draw all the vertical and horizontal lines in one go to save moving your ruler. If in doubt, mark anything with pencil first. The felt-tip or paint will easily go over it. Any grid lines showing can also be painted over.

2. Make a bold edge to the finished work by going round with a thick black line.

HOW TO MAKE A TOGA

Roman men who were citizens wore a **toga**. It was a large semi-circle of woollen cloth draped around the body with a tunic (**tunica**) worn underneath. An emperor's **toga** could be 6 metres long and was dyed bright purple. Women wore a dress called a **stola**. They preferred linen or cotton to wool. Very rich people wore silk specially imported all the way from China.

TOGS IS A SLANG WORD FOR CLOTHES.

YOU'LL NEED:
An old white double sheet, an extra large white T-shirt, 1-metre length of string, drawing-pin, scissors and pencil.

SUBLIGACULUM IS LATIN FOR ROMAN UNDERPANTS.

Drawing-pin half-way across sheet.

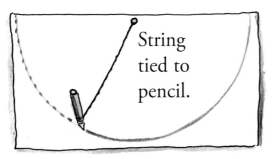

String tied to pencil.

1 Mark out a semi-circle on the sheet using the string and drawing-pin. Cut it out.

2 Put on the T-shirt and use the string as a belt.

3 Hang one end of the **toga** over your left shoulder.

4 Now toss the other end over the top of it.

5 Tuck the middle into the string belt.

TOP TIP – TOP TIP
Never mind if you have a mishap with your **toga** – as long as you're wearing your **subligaculum**!

THE ROMAN EMPIRE

The 2nd Century AD

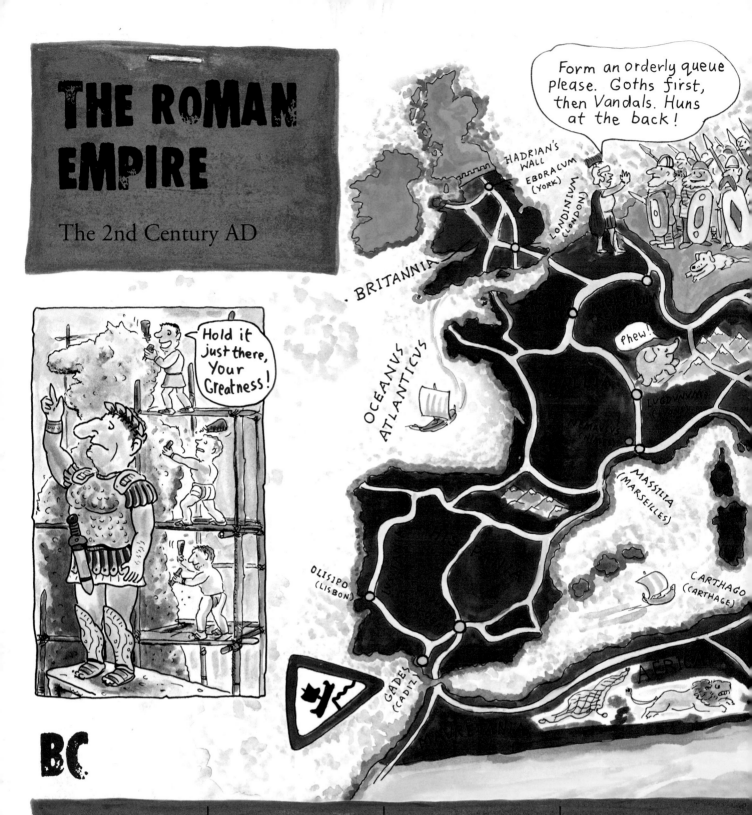

BC

753 BC
The legendary founding of Rome by Romulus, the first king.

509 BC ROME
Rome becomes a republic.

264-146 BC
Wars with Carthage, a rival power in North Africa.

44-27 BC
Julius Caesar is made dictator for life then murdered. Rome becomes an empire, Augustus is the first emperor.

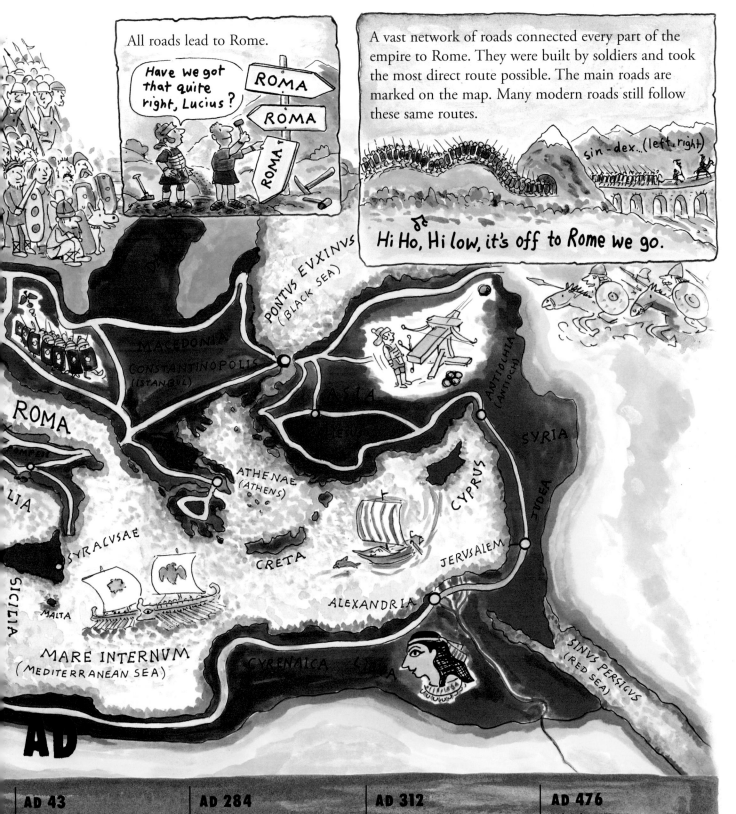

All roads lead to Rome.

Have we got that quite right, Lucius?

ROMA
ROMA
ROMA

A vast network of roads connected every part of the empire to Rome. They were built by soldiers and took the most direct route possible. The main roads are marked on the map. Many modern roads still follow these same routes.

sin - dex...(left, right)

Hi Ho, Hi low, it's off to Rome we go.

PONTVS EVXINVS (BLACK SEA)

MACEDONIA

CONSTANTINOPOLIS (ISTANBUL)

ASIA

ANTIOCHIA (ANTIOCH)

SYRIA

CYPRVS

JUDEA

ROMA

ATHENAE (ATHENS)

CRETA

JERVSALEM

SYRACVSAE

SICILIA

MALTA

ALEXANDRIA

MARE INTERNVM (MEDITERRANEAN SEA)

CYRENAICA

SINVS PERSICVS (RED SEA)

AD

AD 43
Emperor Claudius conquers Britain, the most northerly addition to the empire.

AD 284
Empire is now too big for one ruler. It is split into East and West.

AD 312
Constantine becomes first Christian emperor of Rome. Moves the capital to a new city in the East, Constantinople.

AD 476
The last Emperor in Rome, Romulus, falls. Barbarian tribes sack Rome.

HOW TO MAKE A WATER CLOCK

Romans used sundials to tell the time. It was all right if it was sunny, but imagine trying to tell the time at night. For this they used a water clock (**clepsydra**). They still needed a sundial to mark out the time scale on the water clock.

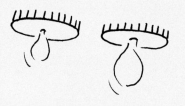

YOU'LL NEED:
A large plastic bottle with top, scissors, strong drawing-pin, stop watch and marker pen.

Nearly time for a drink of water.

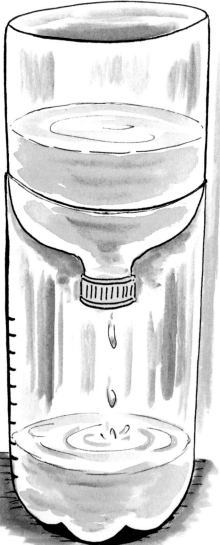

Ancient clepsydra

scale

 1 Ask an adult to help cut the bottle in two.

 2 Make a small hole in the bottle top using the drawing-pin.

3 Upturn the top into the bottom.

4 Pour some water into the top and time how much water drips through in 1 minute, 2 minutes, 3 minutes and so on.

5 Mark the side and make a scale of minutes.

Experiment with the size of hole and bottle to make the most useful clock.

Romans used them to time speeches.

Oh no! Another 15 clepsydra man.

HOW TO MAKE A SHIELD

If you were a Roman soldier in battle, the only thing between you and your enemy's sword was your shield. It was made by sticking layers of wood together and it was curved for strength. Inside was a leather handle protected on the outside by a metal boss.

YOU'LL NEED:

Corrugated cardboard (large TV box), thin card, ruler, 4 large plastic bottles, PVA glue, scissors, craft knife, pens, brushes, acrylic paints and stencils.

TOP TIP – TOP TIP

Glue the two pieces of cardboard together with the corrugation going in opposite ways. This makes it stronger.

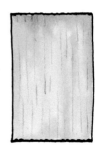

Metal boss

Cut out two sheets of cardboard, 75 x 50 cm.

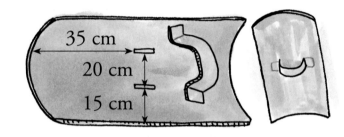

2 Dampen the cardboard sheets with a spray (not too much!) and bend them.

3 Lay them over the plastic bottles to form a curve. Paint the tops with PVA mixed with an equal amount of water. Allow to dry.

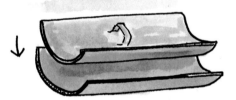

40 cm

10 cm

2.5 cm
5 cm
2.5 cm

35 cm
20 cm
15 cm

4 Make a handle out of corrugated cardboard. Fold over and glue.

5 Make two 5-cm long cuts in one curved sheet and slot the handle into them.

6 Fit both curved sheets together and glue.

7 Cut the bottom off one plastic bottle in a star shape.

8 Fold over the star points and glue to a sheet of thin card. Stick this to the front of the shield.

9 Finish off with acrylic paint and stencils.

HOW TO MAKE A FORT

When the Romans conquered a new country, they had to defend themselves from constant attacks. They built strong forts as bases for Roman soldiers. In AD 122, the Emperor Hadrian had a wall built across northern Britain to stop attacks by barbarians from Scotland. It was 117 kilometres long and 6 metres high. It can still be seen today.

YOU'LL NEED:
Thin card (cereal box), stencils, scissors, ruler, glue, pencil and paints.

SOLDIERS SENT TO BRITAIN FROM WARM COUNTRIES FOUND IT VERY COLD. THEY PUT BITS OF SHEEP'S WOOL BETWEEN THEIR TOES TO KEEP THEM WARM.

TOP TIP – TOP TIP
You can make longer walls by drawing them twice with the stencil.

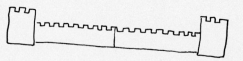

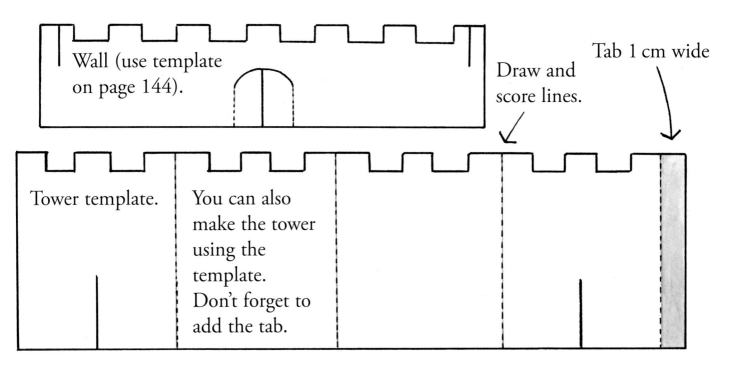

Wall (use template on page 144).

Draw and score lines.

Tab 1 cm wide

Tower template.

You can also make the tower using the template. Don't forget to add the tab.

1 Draw the wall stencil on to card. Cut it out. Copy the tower template on to card. (See the instructions on page 139.)

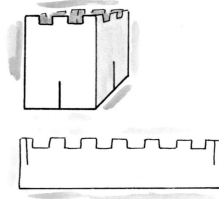

Glue tab here.

2 Cut out and fold the tower like this.

3 Cut a slit in the two sides of the tower which join the walls. Cut a slit in each top end of the wall.

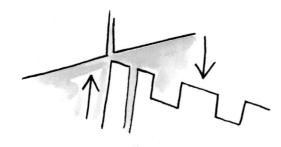

4 Join the walls to the tower by slotting one slit into the other.

5 Join four walls and four towers in a square to make a fort. Draw and make a gate. Paint the fort to look like stone.

HOW TO MAKE A MEAL

In Rome, most people lived in small wooden flats where cooking was banned as a fire hazard. They had to buy takeaways from the local food bar called a **popina**. What a good name! Rich Romans ate a lot. They held enormous feasts where guests lay on couches and stuffed themselves. When they were full up, they could make themselves sick and then continue partying.

BIG C's MORE THAN YOU CAN EAT BUFFET

Indigestion
Sometimes they weren't sure if they had eaten too much or been poisoned!

WERE SOME EMPERORS CRAZY? WE KNOW THAT WINE WAS HEATED AND FOOD WAS COOKED IN LEAD CONTAINERS. FROM WHAT WE KNOW TODAY ABOUT LEAD POISONING, PERHAPS THIS WASN'T A GOOD IDEA!

YOU HAVE TO BE MAD TO RULE HERE

They're coming to take me away... HA HA!

PANIS DULCIS (sweet bread)

YOU'LL NEED:
Wholemeal bread, milk, olive oil and honey.

1 Cut the bread into bite-sized cubes.

2 Dip them in milk.

Yum!

★ Fry quickly in a little olive oil until the outsides are crisp. (Be careful as it may spatter.)

4 Serve straightaway with warmed honey.

STUFFED DORMOUSE

YOU'LL NEED:
At least one not very clever dormouse, earthenware jar and big bag of nuts.

Stuffing: minced pork and minced dormouse (some you might have left over from last time) mixed with asafoetida, (a bitter-tasting plant resin smelling of garlic) and pine kernels.

I'm a dormouse. Get me out of here!

1 Place dormouse in earthenware jar.

2 Feed with nuts until fat (this could take weeks).

3 Kill dormouse.

I'm off!

4 Stuff dormouse, sew up with string and place on a tile in the oven (**fumus**) until done.

HOW TO GET A HOT BATH

These were not just places for a quick splash but somewhere to meet friends and chat. All Roman cities had public baths and toilets. There were separate ones for men and women.

YOU'LL NEED:

One Roman legion, 3,000 slaves, 4 square kilometres of forest with long trees for scaffolding, lots of stones or bricks.

ONE IN THREE NOT FREE

THE POPULATION OF ITALY WAS ABOUT SIX MILLION AND TWO MILLION OF THOSE WERE SLAVES.

STAFF MOTTO

BUILD OR BE KILLED MUCH OF THE BUILDING WORK WAS DONE BY SOLDIERS. IT KEPT THEM OUT OF MISCHIEF WHEN NO FIGHTING WAS GOING ON.

 First build an aqueduct from the nearest mountains.

More ducts and lead pipes take the water to public baths and fountains. Only very rich people had their own water supply.

The aqueduct is built at a slight angle so that the water(s) (**aquae**) flows gently down a stone channel (**ductus**) into the city.

Drinking fountain

SMART!

PUBLIC BATHS

The water is heated in a large stone tank lined with lead.

Slave

Fire

Hypocaust (central heating) warm air flows under the floor and inside the walls.

Warm air

PUBLIC TOILETS

Turned out nice again.

Sponge sticks for wiping.

Waste water flows into the river.

VIKING ACTIVITIES HOW TO MAKE A HELMET

For a Viking in battle against axes and swords, his helmet was his best friend. The basic model came in metal or leather. Added extras included a spike on top, a neck guard and a nose protector. Unfortunately, those fantastic helmets with horns probably never existed on the battlefield.

HARALD THE HOUSE HUSBAND?

See page 130.

1 Fit the long card strip around your head. Glue the ends together.

YOU'LL NEED:
Card: 1 strip 64 x 3 cm and 2 strips 38 x 3 cm, bubble plastic (with small bubbles) 50 x 20 cm, glue, scissors, marker pen, acrylic metallic paints and brush.

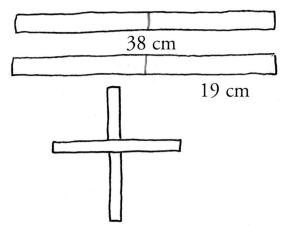

38 cm

19 cm

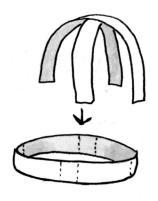

2 Mark the centres of the other two strips, and glue together to form a cross.

3 Position the ends equally inside the headband. Mark and glue.

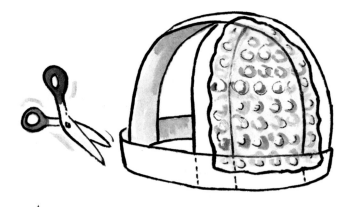

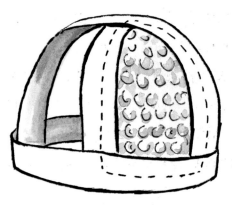

★ Mark and cut out four pieces of bubble plastic 1.5 cm bigger than the spaces between the strips.

5 Glue to the inside of the card strips.

6 Paint to look like metal. Use thick blobs of acrylic paint to look like rivets.

TOP TIP - TOP TIP
You can use shorter strips of card from cereal boxes by sticking two together.

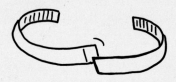

HOW TO MAKE A SHIELD

A Falkyr (or Valkyr) was a Norse war goddess. They flew to earth on their winged horses collecting the dead warriors from the battlefield to live forever with the gods in Valhalla. The Vikings believed the Aurora Borealis was the light glinting off a Valkyr's shields.

YOU'LL NEED:
Corrugated cardboard: 2 x 50-cm square pieces and 1 strip 8 x 30 cm, a 2-litre plastic bottle, PVA glue, ruler, pencil, scissors or craft knife, string, nail, acrylic paints and brushes.

TOP TIP – TOP TIP
Look for pictures of Viking shields to see the different designs painted on them.

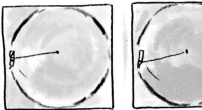

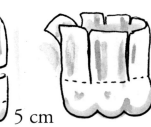

Fold back.

5 cm

1 Use the pencil tied to the nail to draw a circle 50 cm in diameter on the cardboard squares. Cut them out.

2 Cut the bottle in half. Make six equal cuts to the bottom half as shown.

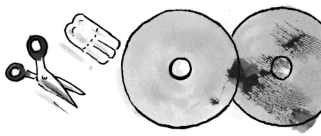

Front

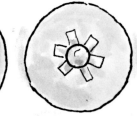

3 Cut bottle-sized holes in the centres of the cardboard circles.

4 Push the bottom of the bottle through one of the holes. Bend over the cut plastic and glue to the cardboard.

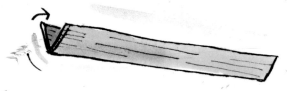
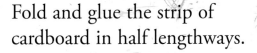

5 Fold and glue the strip of cardboard in half lengthways.

6 Place across the hole and glue.

7 Glue the two circles of cardboard together. Make sure the corrugations go in opposite ways for maximum strength.

8 Finish off with acrylic paint. Write your name on it with runes (see page 136).

119

HOW TO MAKE A MAILSHIRT

The sagas told of the most important Vikings going into battle wearing a byrnie. This was a protective shirt made of interlocking iron rings. Of course, spears and arrows could poke through the holes, so they wore padding underneath - the more the better!

BULKY BYRNIE
A typical sized mailshirt had 30,000 rings and weighed 12 kilogrammes.

← 100 cm →

1 Fold the bubble plastic in half.

2 Lay the T-shirt on top. Draw round it with the marker pen.

★ Carefully cut out the shape and a slot for your head.

4 Tape both sides together as shown.

5 Turn inside out.

6 Paint to look like metal with grey and silver acrylic paint. Wear a belt or weave one (see page 130).

TOP TIP - TOP TIP
Make a berserker bearskin cloak with a piece of brown fun fur. Use a button badge painted gold as a clasp.

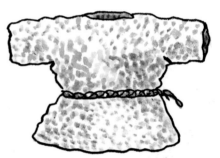

BERSERKERS WERE FEARLESS WARRIORS WHO WORKED THEMSELVES INTO A FRENZY. VERY SCARY!

HOW TO MAKE A WARRIOR'S AXE

Vikings were the first to use the two-handed axe. It certainly scared their enemies and did its job well. The only problem was that while swinging the axe over their heads, their shields got in the way and had to be slung over their back, leaving them an easy target for keen-eyed archers or spearsmen. Ouch!

YOU'LL NEED:
Corrugated cardboard 25 x 50 cm (with corrugations lengthways), card (cereal box) 32 x 15 cm, pencil, masking tape, tracing paper, scissors, ruler, acrylic paints and brushes, stencils, PVA glue.

TOP TIP – TOP TIP
Don't cut through the top fold of the axe head!

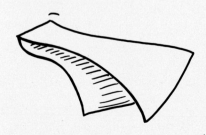

122

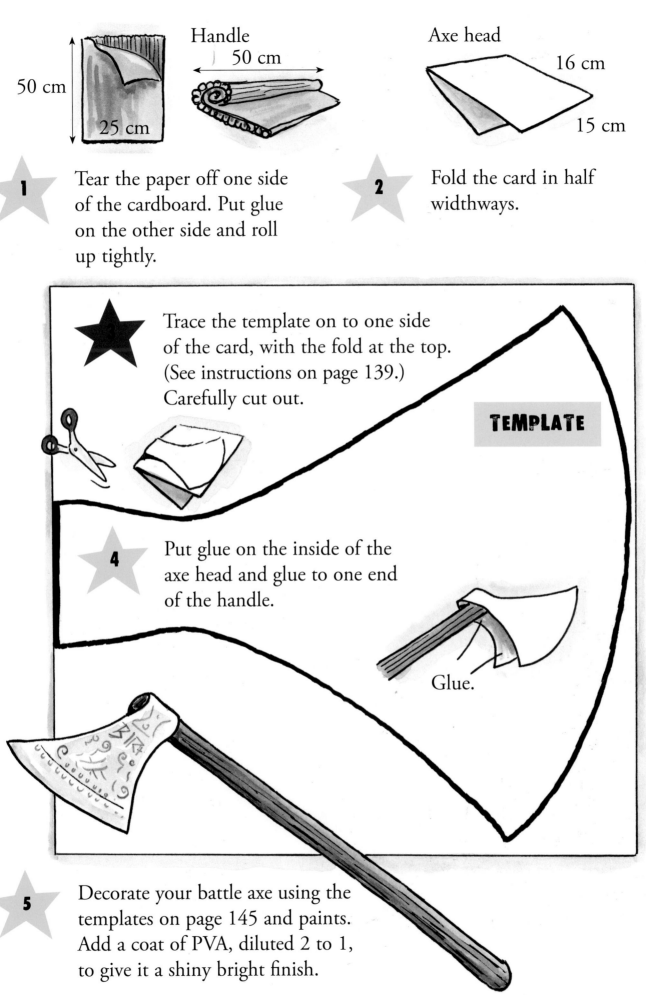

Handle
50 cm

Axe head
16 cm
15 cm

50 cm
25 cm

1 Tear the paper off one side of the cardboard. Put glue on the other side and roll up tightly.

2 Fold the card in half widthways.

3 Trace the template on to one side of the card, with the fold at the top. (See instructions on page 139.) Carefully cut out.

TEMPLATE

4 Put glue on the inside of the axe head and glue to one end of the handle.

Glue.

5 Decorate your battle axe using the templates on page 145 and paints. Add a coat of PVA, diluted 2 to 1, to give it a shiny bright finish.

123

HOW TO DISCOVER AMERICA

The Icelandic Sagas tell the story of Eric the Red, his son, Leif the Lucky, and how they discovered Greenland and America.

YOU'LL NEED:
To discover Greenland first, a nice sturdy longboat, plenty of warriors, some berserkers to frighten the natives, 6 months' supply of dried fish and the luck of the gods.

GREENLAND?
Eric the Red sailed from Iceland to Greenland in AD 982. He called it Greenland to persuade other people to settle there.

The only thing green here is Siggi the Seasick.

VINLAND
About 20 years later, Eric's son, Leif, sailed further west and discovered America. He called it Vinland.

When you see the second polar bear, turn left.

SNORRI BABY

The sagas tell of a baby being born in Vinland. They called him Snorri.

SKRAELINGS

But fierce fighting with the Skraelings, who lived there already, forced the settlers to return to Greenland.

PROOF

In 1960 the remains of a Viking camp were found at L'Anse aux Meadows in Canada. Carbon dating said it was about 1000 years old.

DID VIKINGS STAY IN AMERICA?

Some people think they became part of Native American tribes like the Mandan.

VIKING VOYAGES

Vikings were the best sailors and shipbuilders around. They raided and traded across Europe and the North Atlantic for over 300 years.

EDGE OF THE WORLD

Settlers struggled to live on the icy edge of Greenland for nearly 400 years, then vanished. It could have been because of climate change, disease or fighting with the Skraelings. What do you think happened?

GREENLAND

THAT WAS LUCKY

They settled in Iceland and sailed west to discover Greenland. From there, Leif the Lucky sailed further west and landed in America.

MARKLAND (LABRADOR)

L'ANSE AUX MEADOWS

NEWFOUNDLAND

VINLAND

VIKING RAIDERS

They raided the coasts of the British Isles and France. They set up their own kingdoms in Eastern England, Ireland, the Scottish Islands and Normandy (land of the Northmen).

MAP KEY
➡ Viking voyages
⬤ Viking territory

790–800
Vikings begin raiding the British Isles.

860–
Vikings settle in Iceland.

960–
Harald Bluetooth, King of Denmark and Norway, becomes a Christian.

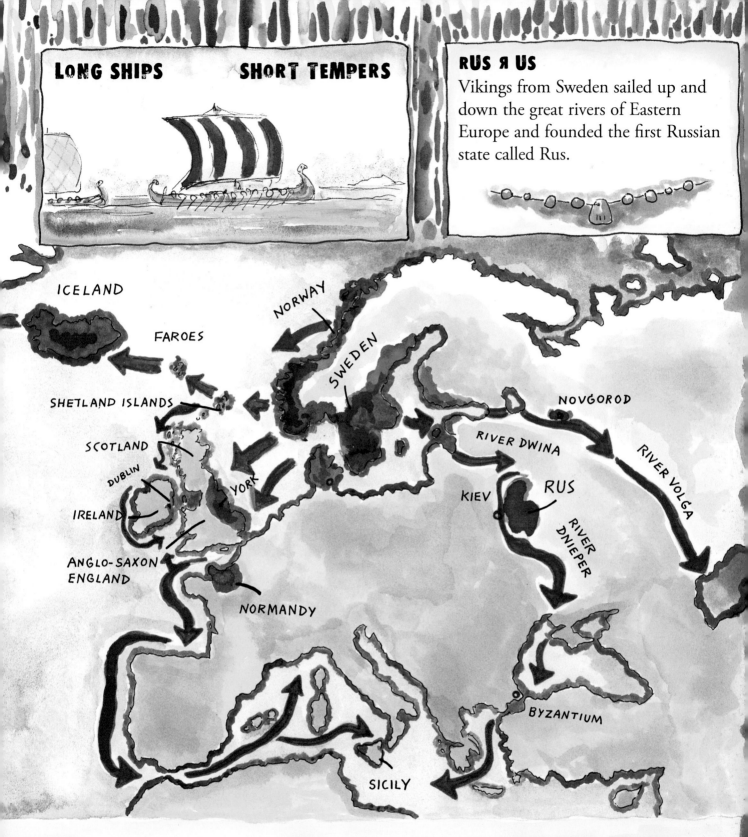

LONG SHIPS   SHORT TEMPERS

RUS Я US

Vikings from Sweden sailed up and down the great rivers of Eastern Europe and founded the first Russian state called Rus.

ICELAND

NORWAY

FAROES

SWEDEN

SHETLAND ISLANDS

NOVGOROD

RIVER DWINA

SCOTLAND

RIVER VOLGA

DUBLIN

YORK

KIEV

RUS

IRELAND

RIVER DNIEPER

ANGLO-SAXON ENGLAND

NORMANDY

BYZANTIUM

SICILY

1000
Leif Eriksson lands
in America.

1066
Harald Hardrada, King
of Norway, killed near York.
The last Viking invasion
of England.

1190-1320
Icelandic Sagas written down.

HOW TO MAKE A VIKING PANCAKE

As well as defending their village while the men were away, Viking women did all the cooking. It was their responsibility to store enough spare food, after harvest or a hunting expedition, to feed their families perhaps for a whole year. Try this pancake and compare it to a modern one. The Vikings used any fruit or berries that were in season.

KITCHENWARE YOU'LL NEED:

Mixing bowl, whisk, dessertspoon, teaspoon, sharp knife, chopping board, non-stick frying-pan, spatula.

INGREDIENTS YOU'LL NEED:

35 g white flour, 30 g wholemeal flour, ¼ teaspoon salt, 175 ml milk, small eating apple, ½ teaspoon butter for each pancake, runny honey to drizzle over. **Makes 5 pancakes of about 11 cm diameter.**

TOP TIP – TOP TIP

Cook one at a time until you get the hang of it.

128

 1 First, wash your hands.

 Wash, core and chop the apple as small as you can.

 3 Mix all the ingredients except the butter and honey together gently.

Get an adult to help with this step. Melt butter in the frying-pan and when it sizzles pour in 3 dessertspoons of batter.

 Cook with a steady sizzle for about 2 minutes each side. Turn it using the spatula.

6 Serve with a drizzle of honey. Take care – they are very hot.

129

HOW TO MAKE A LUCET

The Vikings found a brilliant way to make a single strand of wire or string much stronger. They wound it round a lucet which wove it together to make a long decorative cord. It was an early form of knitting. Done with soft string, the cords could be made into bracelets or drawstrings for bags and purses.

Knut the Knotty wants extra forks and I'm not arguing!

1 Snap the middle prong off the fork to leave only the two end ones.

★ **2** With the fork facing you, wind wool on as shown.

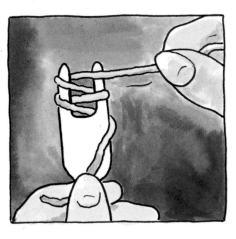

★ **3** Wind it behind the right prong, in front of the left, through to the front and hold out as shown.

★ **4** Push the stitches down with your thumb. Wiggle the lower stitch over the top one and off the prong. Pull the loose end slightly to tighten stitches.

★ **5** Hold the thread out and turn the fork towards you so the back is facing you as in the picture. Wiggle lower stitch over top one again.

★ **6** Keep turning fork round and wiggling bottom stitch over until the chain is long enough. To cast off, cut the wool from the ball, thread through loops and pull it tight.

TOP TIP - TOP TIP
Stick a blob of sticky tack on the fork when you stop so the stitches don't fall off.

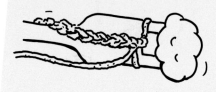

131

GOD DAYS

In English, the names of six days of the week come directly from the old Norse and old English. (The old English is in brackets here.) They replaced the names of the Roman gods, which the days had been named after. Saturday, or Saturn's day, is the odd one out. For a Viking, Saturday was bath day!

 SUNDAY
SOL (SUNNE)

 MONDAY
MANI

Sol, the sun is a girl. Mani, the moon is a boy. They drive their chariots across the sky chased by a pack of savage wolves. If they are caught, the world will end.

 TUESDAY
TYR (TIW)

 **WEDNESDAY**
ODIN (WODEN)

Tyr, the one-handed god of war. Bitten off by the wolf giant, Fenris, who'd love to get hold of the other one.

Odin, riding on his eight-legged horse, Sleipnir, made the world and placed the sun and moon in the sky.

 THURSDAY
THOR

FRIDAY
FREYA and FRIGG

Red-haired son of Odin, makes the thunder and lightning by striking his hammer.

Frigg is the wife of Odin and mother of the Earth. Freya, goddess of love and queen of the elves, rides in a chariot drawn by two giant cats.

 SATURDAY
LAUGAR

Laugar is the old Norse word for 'bath'. Not only bath day, it also belonged to Loki, the god of mischief!

I'm taking my axe, just in case.

SVEN THE SUSPICIOUS MY SAUNA

HOW TO PLAN A VIKING WEEK

Sail through the week with this weekly planner. You can write the date and month on if you like. Each A4 piece of paper will last for two weeks. Then you can replace it with a fresh one.

4 cm x 7

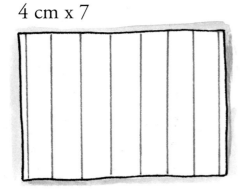

1 Draw lines to divide the A4 paper into seven columns, each 4 cm wide, leaving a small margin.

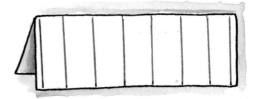

2 Fold in half lengthways.

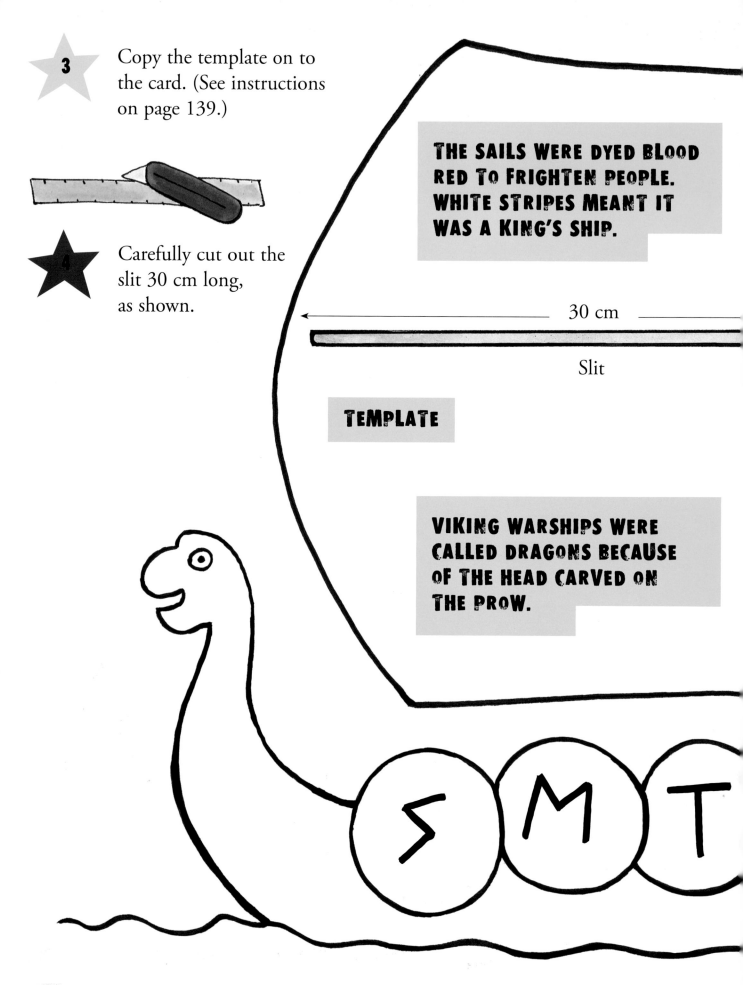

3 Copy the template on to the card. (See instructions on page 139.)

4 Carefully cut out the slit 30 cm long, as shown.

THE SAILS WERE DYED BLOOD RED TO FRIGHTEN PEOPLE. WHITE STRIPES MEANT IT WAS A KING'S SHIP.

30 cm

Slit

TEMPLATE

VIKING WARSHIPS WERE CALLED DRAGONS BECAUSE OF THE HEAD CARVED ON THE PROW.

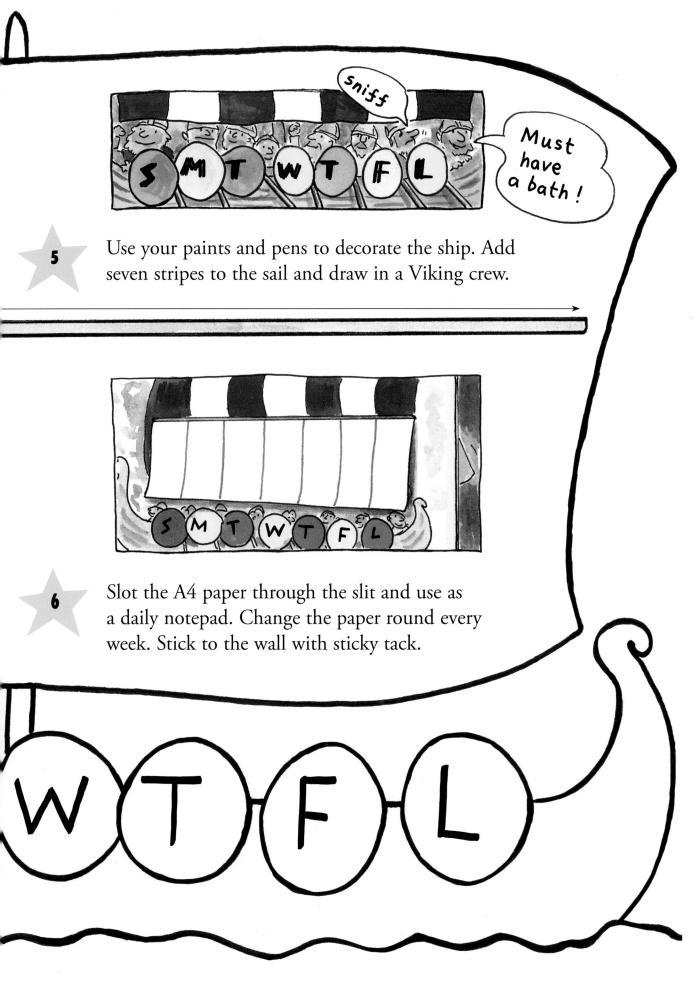

5 Use your paints and pens to decorate the ship. Add seven stripes to the sail and draw in a Viking crew.

6 Slot the A4 paper through the slit and use as a daily notepad. Change the paper round every week. Stick to the wall with sticky tack.

HOW TO WRITE RUNES

The knowledge of the runes was passed to mankind by the Norse gods. 'Rune' means 'secret' and each one has a magical meaning as well as being a letter of the alphabet. They are made of straight lines so they could easily be carved into wood or stone.

YOUR TEMPLATES ON PAGE 145

There were many versions of the runes, but this is one used by the Vikings from about AD 700-1100. It is called FUTHORK after the sounds made by the first six symbols.

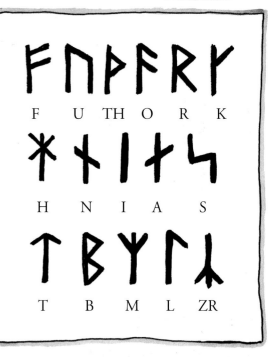

F U T H O R K
F U T H O R K

H N I A S
H N I A S

T B M L ZR
T B M L ZR

If I use my magic ball...

Use this chart to write your name and secret magic spells in runes. There are only 16 symbols, so some are used again for similar sounds.

A	B	C	D	E	F
↑	B	Y	↑	I	F

G	H	I J	K	L	M
Y	*	I	Y	Y	Ψ

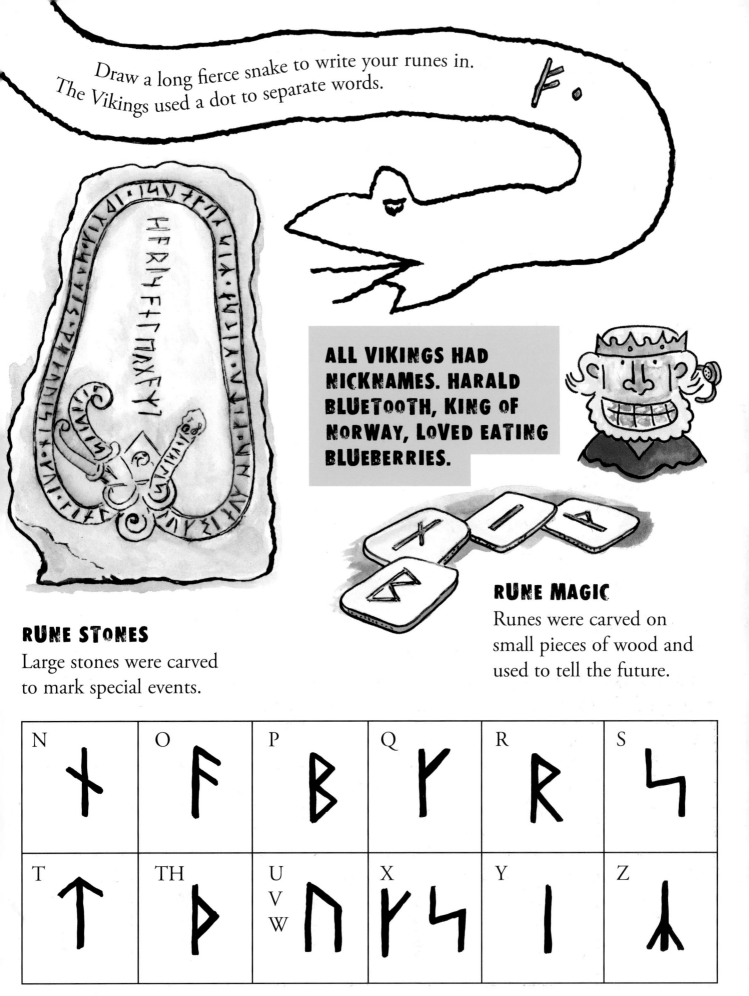

Draw a long fierce snake to write your runes in.
The Vikings used a dot to separate words.

ALL VIKINGS HAD NICKNAMES. HARALD BLUETOOTH, KING OF NORWAY, LOVED EATING BLUEBERRIES.

RUNE STONES
Large stones were carved to mark special events.

RUNE MAGIC
Runes were carved on small pieces of wood and used to tell the future.

N	O	P	Q	R	S
ᛏ	ᚠ	ᛒ	ᛣ	ᚱ	ᛋ

T	TH	U V W	X	Y	Z
ᛏ	ᚦ	ᚢ	ᚼ	ᛁ	ᛉ

TEMPLATES

On the following pages are templates that you can use for some of the activities in this book.

See the opposite page for instructions on how to use them.

HOW TO USE YOUR TEMPLATES

Fix a piece of tracing paper over the template using masking tape. Use a soft, drawing pencil and a ruler, if necessary, to trace the drawing carefully. Turn over the tracing paper and tape it on to card or paper. Use the smooth end of a pen to rub over all the lines on the tracing paper to transfer the image on to the card or paper. Don't worry that it is reversed! Simply cut out the shapes and turn them over. Now you have a set of templates that you can draw around. If you are feeling brave you could try to draw them without the templates straight onto paper or card.

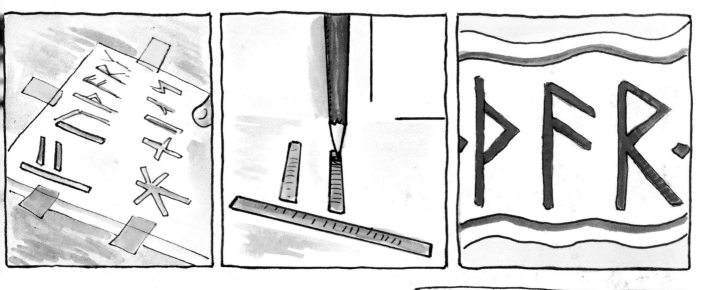

TOP TIP - TOP TIP
Get an ancient wood or stone effect by putting different textured surfaces under your paper.

1 Place the paper on top of your stencil and rub over it with a pencil or crayon. This will give the rune a carved-out look.

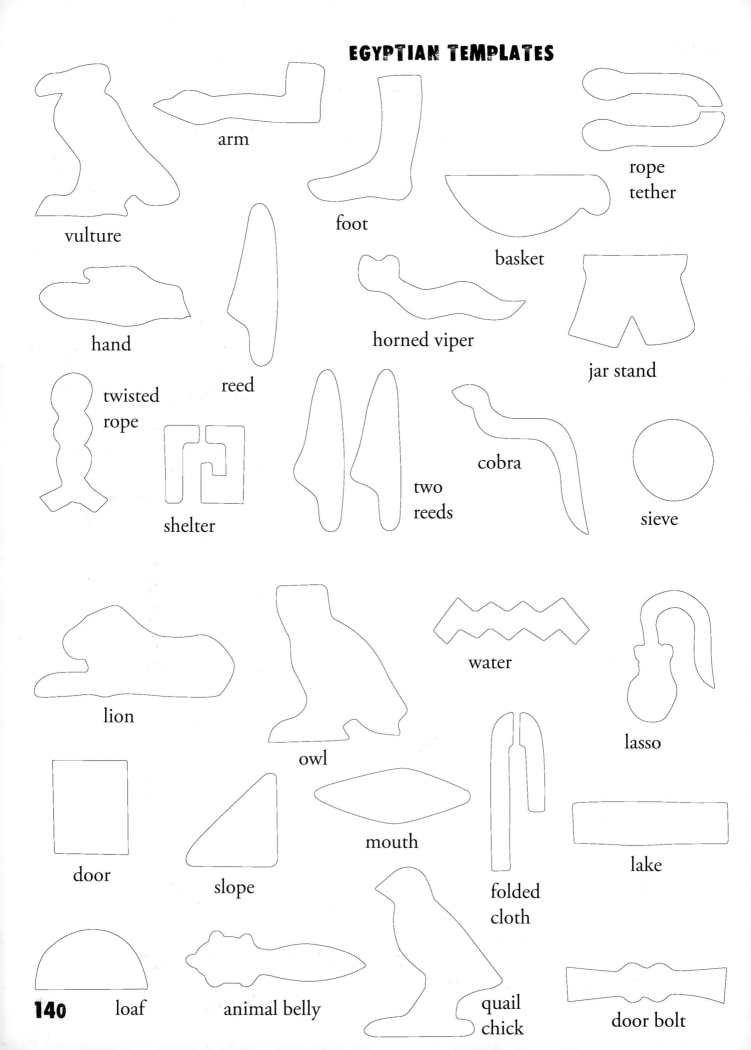

EGYPTIAN TEMPLATES

vulture

arm

foot

basket

rope tether

hand

reed

horned viper

jar stand

twisted rope

shelter

two reeds

cobra

sieve

lion

owl

water

lasso

door

slope

mouth

folded cloth

lake

140 loaf

animal belly

quail chick

door bolt

GREEK TEMPLATES

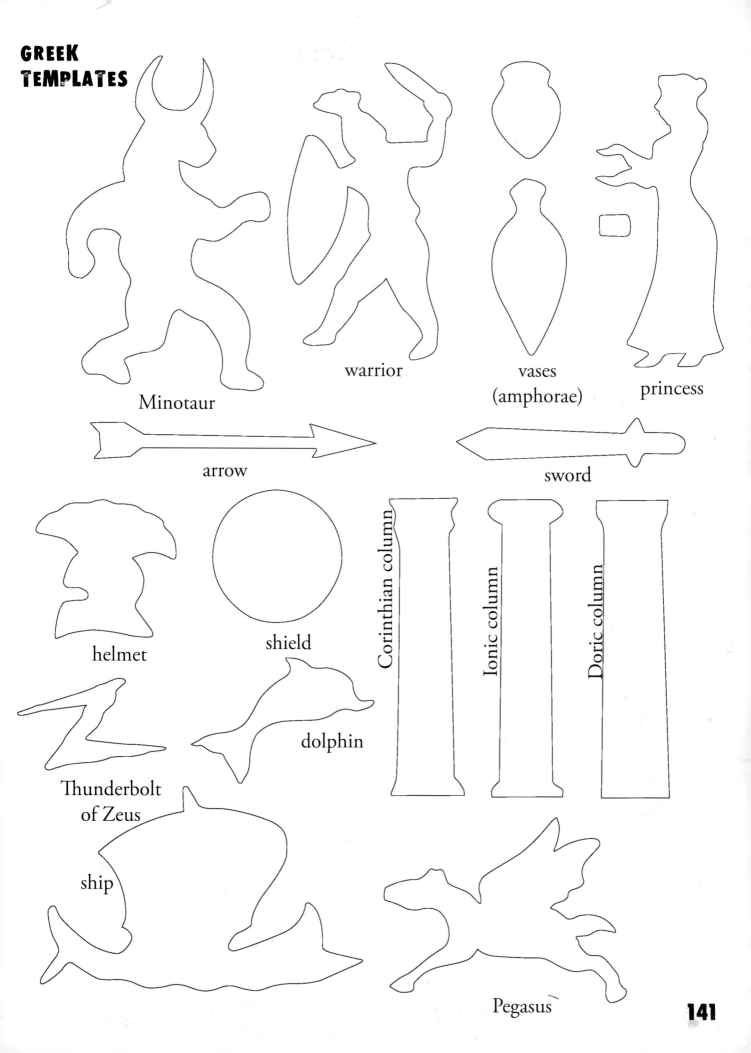

Minotaur

warrior

vases
(amphorae)

princess

arrow

sword

helmet

shield

Corinthian column

Ionic column

Doric column

dolphin

Thunderbolt
of Zeus

ship

Pegasus

MIDDLE AGES TEMPLATES

sword

dragon

lion

heart

star

lozenge

cross

roundel

crescent

bell

fleur-de-lis

shield

sheaf

crown

shamrock

sun

castle

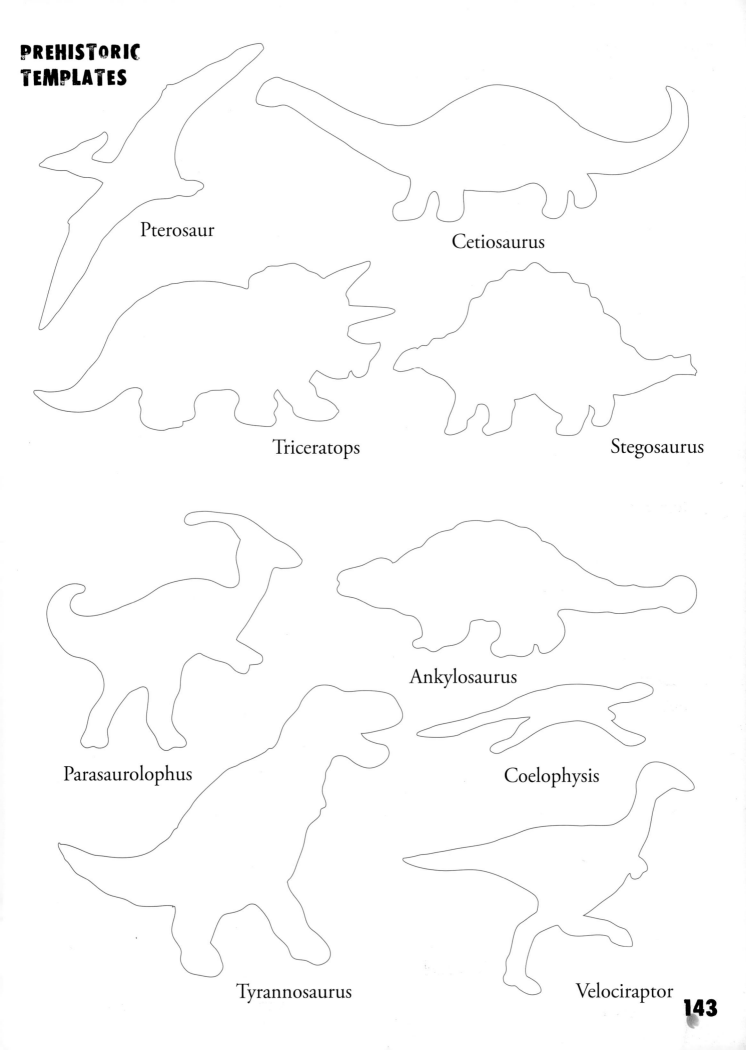

PREHISTORIC TEMPLATES

Pterosaur

Cetiosaurus

Triceratops

Stegosaurus

Parasaurolophus

Ankylosaurus

Coelophysis

Tyrannosaurus

Velociraptor

143

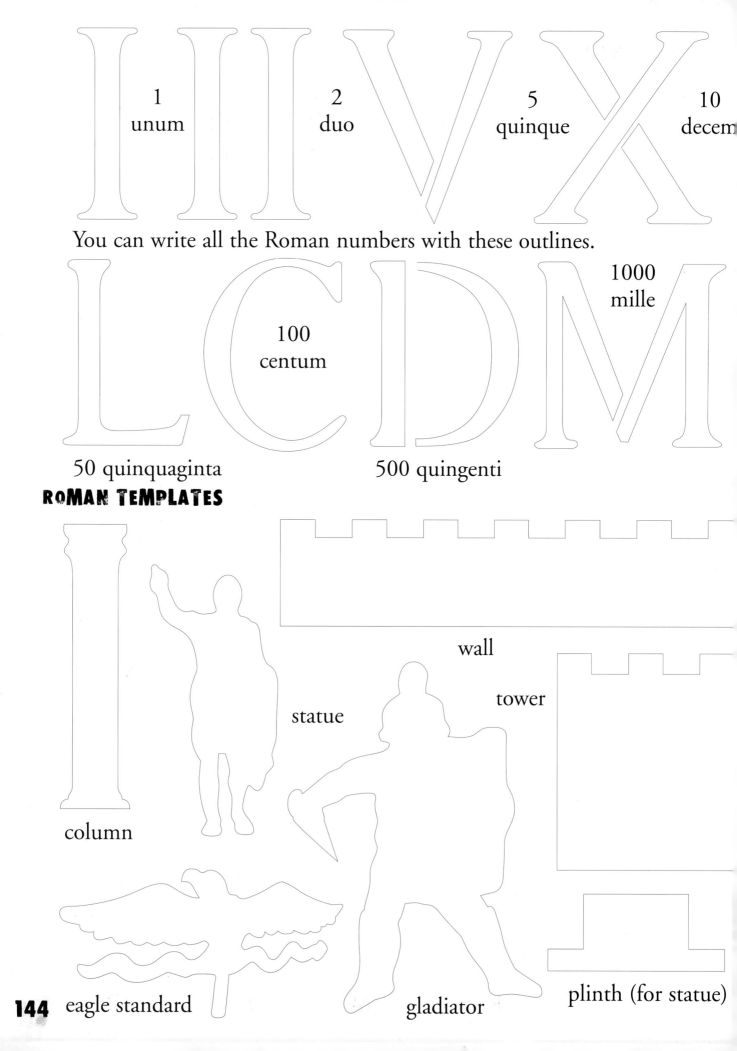

1 unum

2 duo

5 quinque

10 decem

You can write all the Roman numbers with these outlines.

1000 mille

100 centum

50 quinquaginta

500 quingenti

ROMAN TEMPLATES

column

statue

wall

tower

eagle standard

gladiator

plinth (for statue)

VIKING TEMPLATES

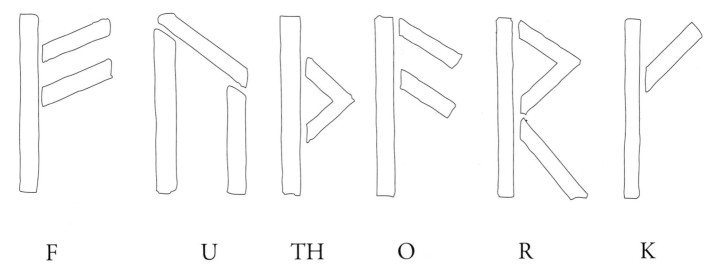

F   U   TH   O   R   K

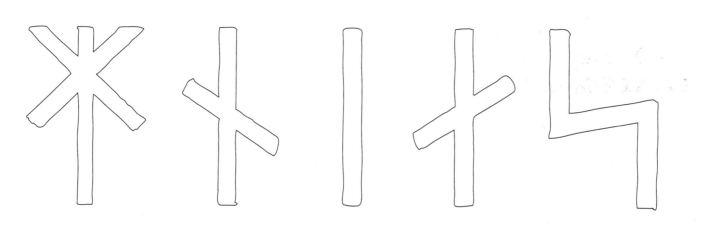

H   N   I   A   S

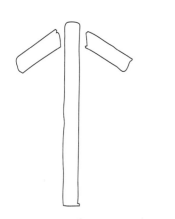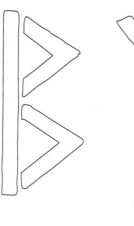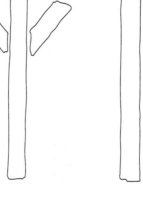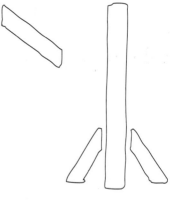

T   B   M   L   ZR

145

GLOSSARIES

AD – stands for Anno Domini.
It means in the time of Our Lord, another name for Jesus Christ.
Years were measured from his birth.

BC – stands for Before Christ.
Time was measured in years leading up to Christ's birth.

DNA – the special information inside each living thing. DNA testing tells us important facts about the living and the dead.

Embalmed – treated with oils and chemicals to stop the body naturally rotting.

Empire – land ruled by one emperor, usually many countries.

Fertilizing – adding plant food to the land to help crops grow.
Nile mud was fertilizing.

Oasis – an area of desert where there is water and plants can grow.

Founding – building where there was nothing before.

Papyrus – tall plants like reeds which grew along the Nile banks.
The Egyptians used the stems to make a kind of paper.

GREEK pages 28-49

Aphrodite – the goddess of love and beauty.

Athene – the goddess of wisdom.

BC – stands for Before Christ. Time was measured in years leading up to Christ's birth.

Besieged – surrounded by an army so that no one could enter or leave. When food and water ran out, the besieged people had to surrender or die.

Epic – a long story telling about the adventures of heroes, often written as a poem.

Gorgons – Three sisters who had snakes for hair.

Hephaestus – the god of blacksmiths. Aphrodite was his wife.

Minotaur – the monster that King Minos kept in a maze and fed with prisoners.

Mortal – a living being that will die one day. Gods were immortal, they could not die.

Pronunciation – how words should be spoken.

Zeus – the king and father of the gods.

Ambassador – an important person sent from one country to another, often as a messenger. It was a very dangerous job.

Battlements – the top of a castle where the walls were cut away in an up-and-down pattern. Archers could shoot at their enemies through the open bits then dodge back behind the walls.

Black Death – a terrible illness that killed eight out of ten people who caught it. It was very catching, spread quickly and had no cure.

Columbus – Christopher Columbus was born in Italy in 1451. He discovered America in 1492 although he thought it was the coast of Asia.

Drawbridge – a sort of door in the castle. It was let down to form a bridge so people could go in or out. It was drawn up quickly if the castle was attacked.

Logo – a small, simple design that is easily associated with a person or thing.

Magna Carta – a very important document that King John of England was forced to sign. It stopped kings having too much power over the people.

Normans – people who came from Normandy in northern France.

Technology – the use of the latest equipment and knowledge. Technology in science means we can test things by carbon dating and DNA to find out how old things are and whether they were related.

'57 Buicks – classic old American cars made in 1957.

PREHISTORIC

Ancestor – family member who lived long before you.

Conservationists – people who protect and preserve.

Ichthyosaur – a dolphin-like reptile, lived in water.

Plesiosaur – a turtle-shaped reptile, lived in water.

Scythe – a curved blade with a handle.

Thrived – lived very well.

PRONUNCIATION GUIDE

Ankylosaurus – an-KY-low-SAW-russ
Cetiosaurus – SEET-ee-oh-SAW-russ
Coelacanth – SEEL-ac-anth
Coelophysis – SEEL-oh-FY-sis
Cretaceous –crut-tay-shuss
Cryptozoology – crip-toe-zoh-OLLER-gee
Ichthyosaur – ICK-theo-SAW
Jurassic – jaw-RASS-ic
Neanderthal – nee-AN -der-tarl
Parasaurolophus – parra-saw-row-LOAF-uss
Plesiosaur – pless-EE-oh-SAW
Pteranodon – terr-AN-oh-DON
Pterosaur – TERR-oh-SAW
Sabre – SAY-ber
Smilodon – SMILER-don
Stegosaurus – STEG-oh-SAW-russ
Triassic – try-ASS-ick
Triceratops – try-SERRA-tops
Tyrannosaurus – tie-RAN-oh-SAW-russ
Velociraptor – vel-OSSY-RAP-ter

Nice croccy!

AD – stands for Anno Domini.
It means in the time of Our Lord, another name for Jesus Christ.
Years were measured from his birth.

BC – stands for Before Christ.
Time was measured in years leading up to Christ's birth.

Barbarian – a savage, uneducated person. The Romans thought that the Goths, Vandals and Huns were barbarians.

Christian – a person who believes in Jesus Christ. He was born under Roman rule with all its cruelty and violence. He taught peace and love.

Citizen – a person who lives as a free man. Citizens are loyal to the country they live in and in return are protected by it.

Dictator – someone who rules with total power.

Empire – land ruled by one emperor, usually many countries.

Founding – building where there was nothing before.

Legendary – to do with a story, nobody knows for certain if it is true.

Republic – a country whose leader is chosen by the people who live there.

Sack – to attack and destroy.

Slave – a person who is owned by another person and has to do whatever that person wishes.

The Latin name for words appears in **bold** type throughout the book.

AD – stands for Anno Domini. It means in the time of Our Lord, another name for Jesus Christ. Years were measured from his birth.

Anglo-Saxons – the people who conquered and ruled what is now England.

Aurora Borealis – natural display of light seen in the northern night sky.

Carbon dating – a scientific way of finding out how old things are.

Christian – a person who believes in Jesus Christ and follows his teachings. He taught peace and love.

Danelaw – this was the half of England ruled by the Danes.

Expedition – a special journey, often to find something.

Founded – built where there was nothing before.

Kingdom – an area ruled by a king or queen.

Oslo – the capital of Norway.

Sagas – stories, usually long and detailed, kept alive by being repeated down through the generations until they were written down.

Settlers – people who set up a place to live.

Skraelings – the name the Vikings gave to Native Americans and Arctic people (or Inuits).

Valhalla – a hall in Asgard, the home of the gods, where there was only happiness.

Published by b small publishing ltd.
text and illustrations © b small publishing ltd. 2014

Design: Louise Millar (based on original design by John Dowling)
Editorial: Susan Martineau and Sam Hutchinson
Printed in China by WKT Co. Ltd.

ISBN 978-1-909767-55-3

www.bsmall.co.uk